ANGLO-SAXON CLASSIC

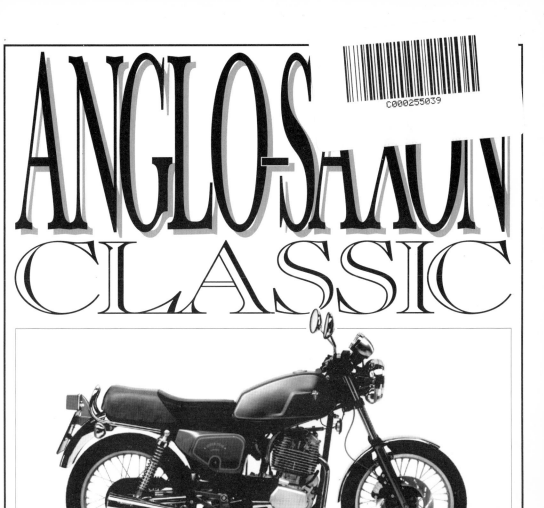

The MZ Silver Star
Modern Technology encapsulated within the fine
Classic style of the Great British Motorcycle.

MZ, long renowned for the German engineering excellence in their famous range of commuter, touring and racing two-stroke machines, have emerged from the transitional period following re-unification with a bright, new and varied range of high quality, attractive machines. The style of the new Silver Star captures the very essence of the Great British Motorcycle, with all the refinements and improvements offered by contemporary design and engineering. The 500cc MZ/Rotax SOHC motor features a four valve head, five speed transmission and electric start, whilst the the chassis boasts all the benefits of modern, high quality frame design, suspension and braking components.

A Thoroughly Modern Classic…

For full information, including a list of our
nation-wide network of friendly dealers, please contact:

**MZ MOTORCYCLE (GB) LTD
ROYCE CLOSE, WEST PORTWAY, ANDOVER,
HAMPSHIRE SP10 3TS**

TELEPHONE: 0264 337443

MILLER'S
Classic
Motorcycles
PRICE GUIDE

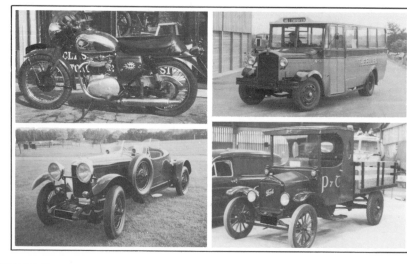

MILLER'S
Classic
Motorcycles
PRICE GUIDE

Consultants
Judith and Martin Miller

General Editor
Jessamy Johnson

1994
Volume I

MILLER'S CLASSIC MOTORCYCLES PRICE GUIDE 1994

Created and designed by
Millers
The Cellars, High Street,
Tenterden, Kent, TN30 6BN
Tel: 0580 766411

Consultants: Judith & Martin Miller

General Editor: Jessamy Johnson
Editorial and Production Co-ordinator: Sue Boyd
Editorial Assistants: Sue Montgomery, Marion Rickman, Jo Wood
Production Assistant: Gillian Charles
Advertising Executive: Elizabeth Smith
Advertising Assistants: Sally Marshall, Liz Warwick
Index compiled by: DD Editorial Services, Beccles
Design: Stephen Parry, Jody Taylor, Darren Manser, John Lonsdale
Additional photography: Ian Booth, Robin Saker

First published in Great Britain in 1993
by Millers, an imprint of
Reed Consumer Books Limited,
Michelin House, 81 Fulham Road,
London SW3 6RB
and Auckland, Melbourne, Singapore and Toronto

© 1993 Reed International Books Limited

A CIP catalogue record for this book is
available from the British Library

ISBN 1-85732-302-5

Bromide output by Final Word, Tonbridge, Kent
Illustrations by G.H. Graphics, St. Leonards-on-Sea
Colour origination by Scantrans, Singapore
Printed and bound in England by Bath Press, Avon

KEY TO ILLUSTRATIONS

Each illustration and descriptive caption is accompanied by a letter-code. By reference to the following list of Auctioneers (denoted by *), Dealers (•) and Clubs (‡), the source of any item may be immediately determined. In no way does this constitute or imply a contract or binding offer on the part of any of our contributors to supply or sell the goods illustrated, or similar articles, at the prices stated. Advertisers in this year's directory are denoted by †.

ADT * ADT Auctions Ltd, Classic & Historic Automobile Division, Blackbushe Airport, Blackwater, Camberley, Surrey. Tel: 0252 878555

ALC * Alcocks, 12 The Crescent, Holmer, Hereford. Tel: 0432 344322

AMOC‡ AJS & Matchless Owners Club, 25 Bevington Close, Patchway, Bristol, Avon.

AOM ‡ Ariel Owners Motor Cycle Club, Swindon Branch, 45 Wheeler Avenue, Swindon, Wilts.

BARC ‡ Bristol & Avon Roadrunners Motorcycle Club, 177 Speedwell Road, Speedwell, Bristol, Avon.

BKS * Robert Brooks (Auctioneers) Ltd, 81 Westside, London SW4. Tel: 071-228 8000

BOC ‡ BSA Owners Club, 44 Foxfield, West Leigh, Havant, Hants.

CM •† Charlie's Motorcycles, 171 Fishpond Road, Bristol, Avon.

CMM Classic Motorcycle Magazine, EMAP National Publications, Bushfield House, Orton Centre, Peterborough.

COB • Cobwebs, 78 Northam Road, Southampton. Tel: 0703 227458

COYS * Coys of Kensington, 2/4 Queens Gate Mews, London SW7. Tel: 071 584 7444

DG • Cedar Classic Cars (Derek Green), Hartley Wintney, Hants. Tel: 0734 326628

DOC ‡ Ducati Owners Club, 131 Desmond Drive, Old Catton, Norwich, Norfolk.

GOC ‡ Goldwing Owners Club, 82 Faley Close, Little Stoke, Bristol, Avon.

HDOC‡ Harley-Davidson Owners Club, 1 St Johns Road, Clifton, Bristol, Avon.

HOLL *† Holloway's, 49 Parsons Street, Banbury, Oxon. Tel: 0295 253197

IMC ‡ Indian Motorcycle Club GB, Surrey Mills, Chilworth, Guildford. Surrey.

LF * Lambert & Foster, 77 Commercial Road, Paddock Wood, Kent. Tel: 0892 832325

LVC ‡ Le Velocette Club, 32 Mackie Avenue, Filton, Bristol, Avon.

LWH •† L W Haggis, 4 Peterhouse Parade, Grattons Drive, Pound Hill, Crawley, Sussex. Tel: 0293 886451

MOC ‡ Maico Owners Club, No Elms, Goosey, Nr Faringdon, Oxon. Tel: 0367 710408

MSL * Michael Stainer Ltd., St Andrew's Hill, Boscombe, Bournemouth. Tel: 0202 309999

MVT ‡ Military Vehicle Trust.

NAC ‡ National Auto-Cycle & Cycle Motor Club, 1 Parkfields, Roydon, Harlow, Essex.

NOC ‡† Norton Owners Club, 47 Pendennis Park, Brislington, Bristol, Avon.

NWB ‡ North Wilts British Motorcycle Club, 20 St Philips Road, Stratton, St Margaret, Swindon, Wilts.

OxM •† Oxney Motorcycles, Rolvenden, Cranbrook, Kent. Tel: 0797 270119

A BSA sidecar body, 1915-1927, painted green with re-trimmed interior. **£200-300** *S*

P * Phillips, Blenstock House, 101 New Bond Street, London W1. Tel: 071-629 6602

PC Private Collection.

RJ * Rogers Jones Co, The Saleroom, 33 Abergele Road, Colwyn Bay, Clwyd. Tel: 0492 532176

ROB • Pete Robson, 1 Gloucester Road North, Filton, Bristol. Tel: 0272 698040

RSS ‡ Raleigh Safety Seven and Early Reliant Owners Club, 26 Victoria Road, Southwick, Sussex.

S *† Sotheby's, 34-35 New Bond Street, London W1. Tel: 071 493 8080

SS ‡ Street Specials Motorcycle Club, 55 Halden Close, Bedminster, Bristol, Avon.

TE • Tennant-Eyles, Barcote Manor, Buckland, Farrington, Oxon.

VER •† Brian Verrall, The Old Garage, High St, Handcross, Haywards Heath, West Sussex. Tel: 0444 400678

VMCC ‡† Vintage Motor Cycle Club, Allen House, Wetmore Road, Burton on Trent, Staffs.

VMSC ‡ Vintage Motor Scooter Club, 11 Ivanhoe Avenue, Lowton St Lukes, Nr Warrington, Cheshire.

ACKNOWLEDGEMENTS

The publishers would like to acknowledge the great assistance given by our consultants.

Malcolm Barber	Sotheby's, 34-35 New Bond Street, London W1A 2AA
Reg Hall	Charlie's Motorcycles, 171 Fishponds Road, Bristol BS3 6PR
David Hawkins	11 Hermes Drive, Burnham-on-Crouch, Essex.
Malcolm Nash	Carole Nash Insurance Consultants Ltd, Paul House, Stockport Road, Timperley, Altringham, Cheshire WA15 7UQ
John Newson	Oxney Motorcycles, Rolvenden, Cranbrook, Kent
Brian Verrall	The Old Garage, High Street, Handcross, Haywards Heath, West Sussex RH17 6BJ

CONTENTS

Key to Illustrations.....5
Acknowledgements.....6
About This Book.....8
State of the Market.....9
Glossary.....10
Insurance Pointers.....11

Acme.....13
AEL.....13
Aermacchi.....13
AJS.....13
Ariel.....17
Baker.....20
BAT.....20
Benelli.....20
BMW.....21
Bradbury.....22
Brough Superior.....22
BSA.....23
Calthorpe.....32
Cotton.....32
Coventry.....32
Dandy.....32
DMW.....32
Douglas.....49
Ducati.....50
EMC Puch.....51
Excelsior.....52
Francis Barnett.....53
Gilera.....53
Harley-Davidson.....54
Harris.....55
Healey.....56
Hesketh.....56
Honda.....56
HRD.....60
Humber.....60
Husqvarna.....61
Indian.....61
Ivy.....61
James.....61
Jawa.....62
Kawasaki.....62
KTM.....63
Laverda.....63
Levis.....63
LMC.....63
Maico.....64
Matchless.....64
Minerva.....66
Morgan.....66
Motobecane.....66
Moto Guzzi.....67
MV Agusta.....68
Moto Morini.....68
Ner-A-Car.....70
New Imperial.....70
Norman.....70

Norton.....71
O.E.C. Blackburne.....76
Overseas.....76
Panther.....76
Parilla Olympia.....77
Puch.....77
Quadrant.....77
Raleigh.....77
Reliant.....79
Rex Acme.....79
Rickman.....79
Royal Enfield.....80
Rudge.....98
Scott.....99
Seeley.....100
Singer.....100
Sun.....100
Sunbeam.....100
Suzuki.....102
Triton.....102
Triumph.....103
Velocette.....109
Vincent.....111
Vindec.....113
WSK.....113
Yamaha.....113
Zenith.....113
Zundapp.....113
Competition Motorcycles.....114
Military Motorcycles.....121
Bicycles.....124
Motorised Bicycles & Autocycles.....124
Tricycles.....126
Mopeds and Scooters.....126
Motorcycle Memorabilia
  Art.....129
  Clothing.....130
  Ephemera
    Magazines.....130
    Programmes.....131
    Posters.....131
    Miscellaneous.....132
Motorcycle Parts.....132
Signs.....132
Miscellaneous.....132

Motorcycle Clubs Directory.....135
Further Reading.....136
Directory of Museums.....140
Index to Advertisers.....142
Index.....143

ABOUT THIS BOOK

Miller's Classic Motorcycles Price Guide presents an overview of the classic motorcycle market place during the past twelve months. In order to give you a comprehensive feel for what is available, we have included illustrations from a wide range of auction houses, dealers, motorcycle clubs and private individuals.

Following the traditional Miller's format, the motorcycles are presented alphabetically by make and chronologically within each make. Competition and military motorcycles, bicycles and autocycles, mopeds and scooters are dealt with in the same way. In the motorcycle memorabilia section, objects are grouped alphabetically by type, for example clothing and ephemera, and then, where possible, chronologically within each grouping. Each illustration is fully captioned and carries a price range which reflects the dealer's/auctioneer's sale price.

The prefix 'Est' indicates the estimated price for the motorcycles which were unsold at auction. Each illustration also carries an identification code which allows the reader to locate its source in the Key to Illustrations.

Please remember Miller's pricing policy: we provide you with a price GUIDE and not a price LIST. Our price ranges, worked out by a team of trade and auction house experts, reflect variables such as condition, location, desirability, and so on. Don't forget that if you are selling, it is possible that you will be offered less than the price range.

Lastly, we are always keen to improve our guides. If you feel that we have left out something important, if you disagree with our panel of experts, or have any other comments about this book, please write and let us know; we value feedback from the people who use this Guide to tell us how to make it even better.

STATE OF THE MARKET

In the course of the last fifteen years, the historic motorcycle market has undergone considerable upheaval in financial terms. In order to understand the changes that have occurred, it is perhaps necessary to first examine the factors that have contributed to the growth in interest and preservation of 'classic' machines.

During the latter part of the 1970s, interest in classic British machines of the 1940s, 50s and 60s flourished. Machines were available at reasonable cost, and the generations who had been in their twenties during these periods found themselves in the position where they could afford to recapture their youth. As a consequence, values rose steadily throughout the early 1980s before finding a level in the mid-1980s at which they stabilised. The market was healthy, although prices were largely below £2,500, except for the genuine exotica.

As the decade drew to a close, speculators who were active in the historic car market, started to show an interest in motorcycles, which inevitably led to increases in prices, although it should be noted that the greatest rises were confined to the prestige models, notably Vincents, which by the autumn of 1989 were realising £25,000 or thereabouts, and Brough Superiors, which were frequently changing hands for figures in the high twenties of thousands. Simply, the market had moved away from its nostalgia base, to an investment orientated one.

However, by the autumn of 1990, certain factors were leading the market into decline, the world recession and economic situation at home resulted in many potential buyers being wary, whilst those who had speculated, in many cases, found that they had overstretched themselves.

This period saw a glut of machines being offered, with prices tumbling. As an example, in the months from September 1990 to September 1991, Vincents, on average, lost £10,000 in value, with a similar pattern being repeated for Broughs, and for much of the other exotica that had seen such dramatic increases during the boom years.

Whilst this was undoubtedly unfortunate for those who had merely sought investment, its effects for enthusiasts were welcome: many machines became affordable again, and the large numbers of the popular models available ensured that any potential buyers could be selective in their choice.

It would appear that 1992-93 has marked a return to the enthusiast-driven market, with prices generally stabilising. One other consequence of the price explosion of the late 80s was the emergence of a market for the hitherto neglected branch of two wheeled transport. Mopeds and autocycles have increased in popularity, as the moped section of this publication demonstrates, whilst the wide variety of styles and levels of sophistication found in this category ensure that there is something for virtually all levels of interest. Equally, lightweights have become increasingly popular, again thanks to their ready availability and comparable low cost.

Another growth area has been in Japanese machines, thanks largely to the teenagers of the 1970s now having the money and desire to recapture their youth on the machines that they rode, or always wished to ride.

Consequently, the movement, or interest, is now probably at its most diverse, with most tastes being catered for.

Although the market is largely enthusiast-driven, it should be remembered that an historic motorcycle is, to a degree, always going to be an investment, in as much as it will always have some monetary value attached to it, although this is likely to fluctuate.

Recent experience suggests that the staple British singles and twins of the 1940s through to the 1960s are best in this respect, having undergone limited fluctuations in price in either direction. This is largely because so many have survived. Equally, most have a reasonable parts supply, helping to reduce restoration costs and ensure future running, whilst specialist clubs abound, catering for all the major marques.

Pre-World War II machines (Pioneer, Veteran, Vintage, etc) also appear to have been less susceptible to market trends, probably as a result of the comparative specialisation that they demand of the owner and consequent limited appeal.

Japanese machines are still largely cheap and readily available, although spares, particularly cycle parts, can be difficult to find, and are often more expensive than similar components for British machines. In conclusion, traditional machines are still good bets, whilst the exotic will always be more vulnerable to market forces. However, in choosing a machine, perhaps the most important thing to remember is to buy what appeals to you, whilst considering spares availability, usage, and the potential cost of any restoration.

GLOSSARY

We have attempted here to define some of the terms that you will come across in this book. If there are any terms or technicalities you would like explained or you feel should be included in future, please let us know.

ACU - Auto Cycle Union, who control a large part of British motorcycle sport.

Advanced ignition - Ignition timing set causing firing before the piston reaches centre top, variation is now automatic.

Air-cooling - Most motorcycles rely on air-cooling to the atmosphere.

Air intake - The carburettor port admitting air to mix with fuel from the float chamber.

AMCA - Amateur Motor Cycle Association, promoters of English off-road events.

APMC - The Association of Pioneer Motor Cyclists.

Auto Cycle Club - Formed in 1903 it was the original governing body of motorcycle sport, in 1907 became the Auto Cycle Union.

Automatic inlet valve - Activated by the engine suction. Forerunner of the mechanically operated valve.

Balloon tyres - Wide section, low pressure, soft running tyres, used on tourers for comfort.

Beaded-edge tyres - Encased rubber beads in channel on wheel rim.

Belt drive - A leather or fabric belt from engine or gearbox to rear wheel.

BHP - A measure of engine output, eg to lift 33,000lb one foot in a minute requires one horsepower.

BMCRC - British Motor Cycle Racing Club, formed in 1909.

BMF - British Motorcycle Federation.

Bore/stroke ratio - Cylinder diameter ratio to stroke.

Cam - Device for opening and closing a valve.

Camshaft - The mounting shaft for the cam, can be in low, high or overhead position.

Carburettor - Used to produce the air/fuel mixture.

Chain drive - Primary form of drive from engine to gearbox and secondary gearbox to rear wheel.

Combustion chamber - Area where the fuel/air mixture is compressed and fired, between piston and cylinder head.

Compression ratio - The fuel/air mixture compression degree.

Crankcase - The casing enclosing the crankshaft and its attachments.

Crankshaft - The shaft for converting the up-and down piston motion into rotary.

Cylinder - Containing the piston and capped by the cylinder head, is the site of the explosion which provides power.

Cylinder head - In a vertical engine caps off the top end of the cylinder. In a 4 stroke engine carries the valves.

Damper - Used for slowing down movement in suspension system or as crankshaft balance.

Displacement - The engine capacity or amount of volume displaced by the movement of the piston from bottom dead centre to top dead centre.

Distributor - A gear driven contact sending high tension current to spark plugs.

DOHC - Double overhead camshaft.

Dry sump - Two oil pumps, one supplying oil to the bearings from a tank, the other to return it to the tank.

Earles forks - An unusual front fork design. A long leading link and rigid pivot through both links behind the wheel.

Featherbed - A Norton frame, designed by Rex and Crommie McCandless, Belfast, used for racing machines from 1950, road machines from 1953.

FIM - Federation Internationale Motorcycliste, controls motorcycle sport worldwide.

Flat head - A flat surfaced cylinder head.

Flat twin - An engine with 2 horizontally opposed cylinders, or 4 to make a Flat Four.

Float - A plastic or brass box which floats upon the fuel in a float chamber and operates the needle valve controlling the fuel.

Flywheel - Attached to the crankshaft this heavy wheel smooths intermittent firing impulses and helps slow running.

Friction drive - An early form of drive using discs in contact instead of chains and gears.

Gearbox - Cased trains of pinion wheels which can be moved to provide alternative ratios.

Gear ratios - Differential rates of speed between sets of pinions to provide higher or lower rotation of the rear wheel in relation to the engine.

GP - Grand Prix, an international race to a fixed formula.

High camshaft - Mounted high up on the engine to shorten the pushrods in an ohv formation.

IOE - Inlet over exhaust, a common arrangement with an overhead inlet and side exhaust.

Leaf spring - Metal blades clamped and bolted together, used in suspension many years ago.

Magneto - A high tension dynamo producing current for the ignition spark. Superseded by coil ignition.

Main bearings - Bearings in which the crankshaft runs.

Manifold - Collection of pipes supplying mixture or taking away fumes.

MCC - The Motor Cycling club which runs sporting events. Formed in 1902.

Moped - A light motorcycle of under 50cc with pedals attached.

OHC - Overhead camshaft, can be either single or double.

OHV - Overhead valve engine.

Overhead cam - An engine with overhead camshaft or camshafts operating its valves.

Overhead valve - A valve mounted in the cylinder head.

Pinking - A distinctive noise from an engine with over-advanced ignition or inferior fuel.

Piston - The component driven down the cylinder by expanding gases.

Post-vintage - A motorcycle made after December 31, 1930 and before January 1, 1945.

Pressure plate - The plate against which the clutch springs react to load the friction plates.

Pushrods - Operating rods for overhead valves, working from cams below the cylinder.

Rotary valve - A valve driven from the camshaft for inlet or exhaust and usually a disc or cylinder shape. For either 2 or 4 stroke engines.

SACU - Scottish Auto Cycle Union, which controls motorcyle sport in Scotland.

SAE - Society of Automotive Engineers. Used in a system of classifying engine oils eg SAE30, IOW/50 etc.

Shock absorber - A damper, used to control up-and-down movement of suspension or to cushion a drive train.

Swinging arm - Rear suspension by radius arms carrying the wheel and attached to the frame at the other end.

Torque - Twisting rotational force in a shaft, can be measured to show at what point an engine develops most torque.

CLASSIC MOTORCYCLE INSURANCE POINTERS

Insurance for the motorcyclist is probably a lot more important than for a car driver, as in an accident, the motorcyclist will nearly always come off second best.

As a result, it is vital to find the correct policy for the type of motorcycle or motorcycles that you own. Over the past two years, the number of insurers of motorcycles has decreased, but if you are prepared to spend time looking around, there are a number of different policies available.

The most vital part about an insurance policy for a classic motorcycle is the agreed value. This means that in the event of a total loss claim, be it accident, fire or theft, the value that has been agreed by the insurers and that appears on the schedule will be the amount paid out, less the policy excess. An agreed value is usually established by submitting valuations from recognised dealers or photographs of the motorcycle to be insured.

Valuation can pose a number of problems, as occasionally a motorcycle that is a common model may have received a 'money no object restoration', which could mean that the final cost of the restoration is way in excess of the true value of the motorcycle. There is also the problem of a bike that is a 'one-off model' or the only one in existence, as there is nothing that it can be compared with in the market. How can a bike like this be valued? Fortunately, there are a number of experts who are willing to help in cases like these, but ultimately it is a matter of personal opinion.

One problem the Insurance Companies have at present with regards to value is that some motorcycles are insured on values based on the price boom of the 1980s. While motorcycles did suffer from the price slump of the early 1990s, in fact only the most expensive and sought-after had their values vastly reduced. On the whole, most policyholders have taken the recession into account and have reduced their insured values, which in turn gives them a slight saving on the premium.

If you have spent the winter meticulously restoring a motorcycle yourself to your own specifications, the last thing you want is to be involved in an accident. However, having restored the machine yourself originally, you may wish to carry out the repairs yourself and a policy which enables you to do this has proved very popular. It means the policyholder can make the repairs in his own time to his own original specification, and the Insurance Company can settle the claim quickly and easily.

Another clause in a policy for classic motorcycles is a buy back clause. This means that if the motorcycle is in a total loss accident, the insured has the option to buy back the salvage from the Insurance Company using the remainder of the settlement of the claim to carry out the restoration.

A traditional policy is the rider policy. This covers any number of bikes owned by the policyholder up to a stated cc limit. This can be a useful type of policy for somebody who tends to change their motorcycle on a regular basis, but it is aimed principally at the owner of current models as any claim made under this policy would be settled on a market or book value basis, with no agreed value being written into the policy.

A common oversight when insuring a vintage motorcycle is only to insure against third party fire and theft on the theory that 'I bend it, I mend it'. It is important to remember that, although it is very rare for parts to be completely unobtainable, this can happen. However, a positive point is that the accidental damage section of comprehensive cover should cover the cost of any spare parts required.

Finally, when insuring your classic motorcycle, remember that it is not the price of the policy that matters, but what you get for your money. A number of brokers have sprung up claiming to be Motorcycle Insurance Specialists, who in fact know very little about motorcycles. When asked for a quote on a Flying Squirrel they are more likely to point you to their 'pet and livestock' policy! If you are in any doubt, join a relevant owners' club and liaise with club members who have similar machines and ask where they are insured.

Malcolm Nash
Carole Nash Insurance Consultants Ltd

ACME

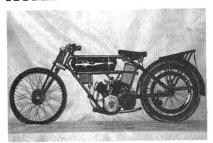

c1913 Acme 557cc Solo Motorcycle.
Est. £500-700 *S*

The Coventry Acme Motor Co. Ltd of Earlsdon, produced motorcycles from 1902-22 before amalgamating in that year with the local Rex Motor Manufacturing Co. to produce the Rex-Acme.

AEL

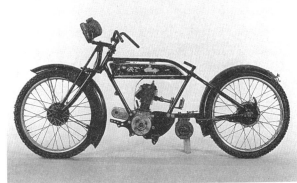

c1922 AEL 348cc Motorcycle, fitted with a side valve Blackburn engine and Albion gearbox.
£200-300 *S*

AEL machines were produced in Coventry by a motorcycle and accessories dealer of the same name from proprietary components between 1919-24.

AJS, England, 1909-

- The first AJS motorcycle was built in 1909 by the Stevens brothers, Harry, George, Jack and Joe.
- In 1927, AJS introduced racing engines with chain driven overhead camshafts and 3-speed gearboxes.
- In 1931, the Stevens brothers sold AJS to the manufacturers of Matchless. This company became known as Associated Motor Cycles Ltd, and subsequently bought Sunbeam and amalgamated with James, Francis-Barnett and Norton.
- AJS has not totally disappeared. A new company, headed by Fluff Brown, is producing Andover 248cc and 358cc 2-stroke moto-cross machines.

AERMACCHI

1972 Aermacchi 350 Sprint Solo Motorcycle, finished in traditional Aermacchi red livery, frame/engine No. 252927.
Est. £1,800-2,200 *S*

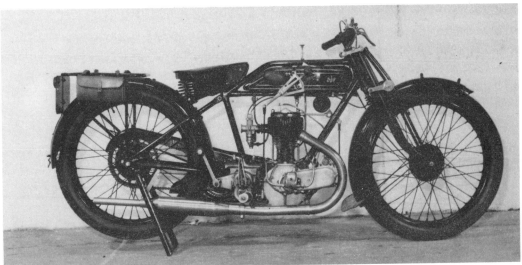

1927 AJS 350cc Motorcycle.
Est. £2,000-2,500 *S*

This machine has been on display in Holker Hall Museum and during the late 1920s and early 1930s won several gold medals in the hands of Lady Louis Maclain.

1927 AJS H8 500cc Motorcycle,
with a **1924 Swallow No.2
Sidecar.**
£9,000-11,000 *PC*

*In the 1920s A.J. Stevens
annually changed and modified
their models. Most components
were stamped with a letter. The
'H' part of H8 is the letter for
1927. 'G' being 1926 and 'K' 1929.
They were noted for their light
weight with good performance and
handling.*

Locate the Source

*The source of each
illustration in Miller's can
be found by checking the
code letters below each
caption with the list of
contributors.*

1931 AJS 250cc Motorcycle,
dynamo missing.
£800-1,000 *S*

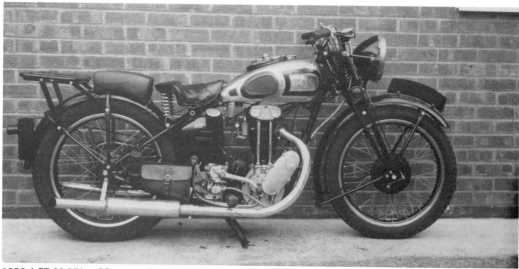

1936 AJS 22 250cc Motorcycle.
£2,000-4,000 *NAC*

*Very few examples of this year and
model exist.*

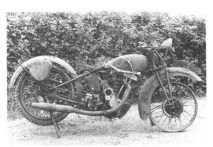

c1934 AJS B6 350cc Motorcycle.
£350-400 *S*

The AJS B6 'Sloper' was listed for 1934, a big port sports model with pushrod overhead valves.

1953 AJS 7R 350cc Motorcycle, fitted with 1949 engine.
£4,000-4,500 *S*

Although designed purely as a racing machine the power plant found its way into a number of scrambler specials where it proved to be very competitive while a small number of machines were adapted for road use by enthusiastic owners.

1952 AJS Model 18 500cc Motorcycle.
£1,400-1,600 *S*

1950 AJS 7R 350cc Motorcycle.
£10,000-13,000 *VER*

1953 AJS 16MS 350cc Motorcycle.
Est. £1,300-1,600 *S*

One of the definitive post war British singles the 16MS and its Matchless cousin, the G3LS, adopted the distinctive AMC made jampot rear suspension units in 1951, at a time when many of their competitors still relied on, at best, plunger rear suspension, or at worst, a rigid back end.

1957 AJS Model 30 Spring Twin 600cc Motorcycle.
£2,000-2,500 *NWB*

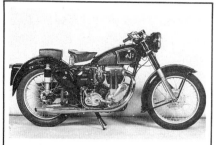

1952 AJS 18S 500cc Motorcycle.
Est. £2,500-2,800 *S*

Produced alongside Matchless's G80S, the AJS 18S enjoyed a production run from 1949 to 1963. In 1952 the 18S sold for £215.6s.1d. and in CS form achieved significant competition success. 1951 saw a big step forward in design with the introduction of jampot suspension, alloy cylinder head and pushrods and the adoption of the Burman gearbox for the entire AMC range. The 18S developed 23bhp at 5,400rpm.
The bike was exhibited in the Norman Ball Transport Collection Museum on the Isle of Wight.

1953 AJS 18S 'Green Laner' 500cc Motorcycle.
£1,800-2,200 *AMOC*

1959 AJS 14 250cc Motorcycle.
£1,300-1,700 *AMOC*

1960 AJS Model B1 650cc Motorcycle, black and chromium finish.
£1,750-1,950 *S*

c1965 AJS 50cc Solo Motorcycle and Sidecar, child's fun vehicle.
£1,250-1,500 *ADT*

This vehicle was manufactured in c1965 and is a converted Raleigh Dream motorcycle. Using a Villiers engine of about 50cc capacity, the machine has been altered so that it now houses an AJS petrol tank and period looking box sidecar.

ARIEL, England, 1902-70

- Built De-Dion engined three-wheelers in Birmingham in 1898 and 4 years later began to manufacture motorcycles with 3.5hp single cylinder White and Poppe engines.
- In 1927, Ariel was joined by the technician Edward Turner, who subsequently designed the well known Square Four.
- Also, at that time, the chief designer was Val Page who designed the Leader and the Arrow.
- Famous Ariel trials riders include Harold Perry, Fred Povey, Ted Ray, Ron Langston and the famous Sammy Miller.

1930 Ariel Model A 550cc Motorcycle, 4 stroke, single side valve.
£2,500-3,000 *AOM*

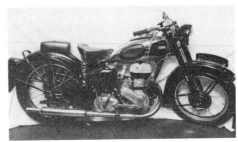

1946 Ariel 600cc Solo Motorcycle, side valve, 4 stroke.
£2,000-2,500 *ROB*

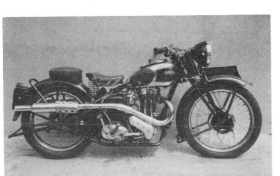

1939 Ariel Red Hunter 350cc Motorcycle.
£3,200-3,500 *VER*

Introduced in 1932, Ariel's Red Hunter was offered as a sporting version of their overhead valve 4 stroke bikes and, as well as being subject to steady development by the factory over its long production run, the Red Hunter lent itself to modification and development by the enthusiastic amateur.

1949 Ariel Square Four MkI 997cc Motorcycle, 4 stroke, 4 cylinder.
£2,500-3,000 *AOM*

1948 Ariel Square Four 4G 995cc Motorcycle, finished in maroon and featuring a rigid rear end.
£2,200-2,500 *S*

In 1936 Edward Turner, who later became the boss of Triumph, creating for them the famous speed twin, and later joining BSA, for whose Daimler subsidiary he designed the Daimler V8 engine, developed the 1000cc Squariel which established Ariel's success in the big bike market. The bike offered low speed tractability in top gear and punchy acceleration to its top speed of 100mph.

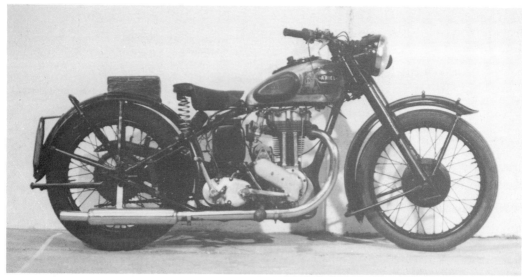

1948 Ariel 350cc NH Redhunter Motorcycle.
£600-1,000 *S*

With the return to peacetime production Ariel announced a range of six machines including the NG and VG singles in 350cc and 500cc respectively, and their more sporting cousins the NH and VH Red Hunters which featured a larger carburettor and cleaned up internals to improve performance. The image was further enhanced with some extra chrome plating.

1951 Ariel Square Four MkI 1000cc Motorcycle.
Est. £2,800-3,500 *S*

This example dates from 1951, and was owned by the Museum of Science & Industry in Birmingham. It has latterly been on display in the Midland Motor Museum.

1955 Ariel Huntmaster 650cc Motorcycle, 4 stroke, twin engine.
£2,500-3,000 *AOM*

1962 Ariel Arrow 250cc Motorcycle, good condition.
£8,000-12,000 *HOLL*

1956 Ariel Square Four MkII 1000cc Motorcycle and Watsonian Sidecar.
£7,500-8,500 *S*

This example features Earles forks, a higher compression ratio, an oil cooler and a belt drive. The Watsonian G.P. sidecar has been colour matched to the motorcycle's traditional maroon.

1959 Ariel Square Four 1000cc Motorcycle.
£3,800-4,500 *VER*

1963 Ariel Leader 250cc Motorcycle, red and cream paintwork.
£300-500 *S*

1963 Ariel Sports Arrow 250cc Motorcycle.
£250-350 *S*

1957 Ariel Square Four MkII 1000cc Motorcycle Combination with Watsonian Sidecar.
Est. £3,850-5,000 *S*

Previously owned by the Museum of Science & Industry in Birmingham, the motorcycle has been stripped completely and rebuilt and has been on display at the Midland Motor Museum.

Ariel adopted the slogan 'Styled for today with a View to Leisure' for its distinctive range of motorcycles in the 1960s. The Leader and the Arrow were produced at the same time, the Arrow being the more sporting and less enclosed of the two bikes and selling for about £30 less than the more sedate looking Leader.

1961 Ariel Arrow 250cc Motorcycle, twin engine.
£1,000-1,400 *AOM*

This motorcycle is fitted with period panniers and a dolphin fairing.

1964 Ariel Leader 250cc Motorcycle, 2 stroke, twin engine.
£1,250-1,500 *AOM*

BAKER

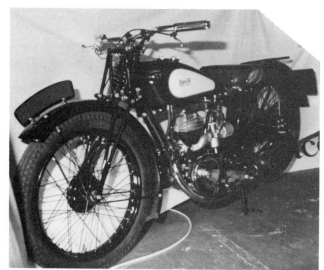

1928 Baker 250cc Motorcycle,
restored to concours standard.
£1,400-2,200 *TE*

The Baker company produced high quality lightweight motorcycles between 1927-1930. They were subsequently taken over by James.

BAT

1912 BAT 8hp Model No. 3 964cc Motorcycle Combination, finished in grey, green and black livery.
£8,500-9,500 *S*

Founded in 1902 by Samuel Batson, BAT motorcycles achieved an enviable reputation for performance from the outset, holding in their first year every speed record from one to fifty miles and by the time that T.H. Tessier took over control in 1905 BAT had introduced motorcycling's first sprung frame.

BENELLI

1977 Benelli 750 SEI Motorcycle.
Est. £3,500-3,800 *S*

Benelli's 750cc SEI 6 cylinder machine was designed to compete with the Japanese 'superbikes' that were increasingly dominating the large capacity market. Unfortunately, delays in production resulted in poor sales.

c1979 Benelli 650S Tornado Motorcycle.
Est. £2,250-2,750 *P*

Benelli, now owned by Moto Guzzi, still produce a small number of motorcycles, the last being 900cc 6 cylinder. Founded in Italy in 1911 by the six Benelli brothers, Benelli have earned themselves a name in history with their great motorcycling works.

BMW, Germany, 1923-

- Founded in 1916 as an aircraft engine factory, the Bayerische Moteren Werke entered the motorcycle trade in 1921.
- The first BMW motorcycle was designed in 1923 by Friz, with shaft drive, a triangular duplex frame and a leaf spring fork. It also had the 493cc engine, in a unit with the gearbox and was transverse mounted.

- From 1928 BMW produced supercharged machines for the works riders which won races all over the world, as well as breaking the world speed record several times between 1929 and 1937 with Ernst Henne riding.
- BMW no longer competes officially in races, but BMW riders are still enjoying success in long distance events.

1952 BMW R25/2 245cc Motorcycle.
£1,500-2,000 *S*

Introduced in 1948, the R25 was largely responsible for BMW's post-war revival.

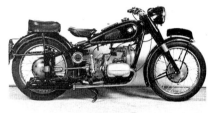

1940 BMW R51 500cc Motorcycle, period rubber saddle and black livery.
£4,200-4,800 *S*

The post-war BMW models, owing to their superior quality, found favour with the discerning enthusiast.

1958 BMW R50 Combination.
Est. £5,000-6,500 *LF*

BMW's R50, although expensive, met with considerable success thanks to the company's high quality and the 'boxer' engine's ability to cover long distances at high speeds without distress.

1959 BMW R50 490cc Motorcycle.
£2,500-3,500 *S*

1973 BMW R75/5 750cc Motorcycle, traditional black livery with white lining.
Est. £1,250-1,500 *S*

1987 BMW R80 RT 800cc Motorcycle.
Est. £1,300-2,500 *S*

BRADBURY

Highly regarded for their quality and hill climbing ability, the Oldham produced Bradbury featured an integral crankcase and frame with the option of a 2-speed, NSU-type gearbox with a 'coffee grinder' control.

1912 Bradbury 500cc Motorcycle.
£6,500-7,500 *VER*

BROUGH SUPERIOR

1938 Brough Superior SS80 and Launch Sidecar, 1000cc.
£9,500-11,500 *VER*

Brough's sidecar machine featured first a JAP and later a Matchless V-twin engine.

1928 Brough Superior 680 Motorcycle, overhead valve.
£11,000-13,000 *VER*

Advertised by George Brough as 'the Rolls-Royce among motorcycles', Broughs were built using only the highest quality components. Testimony to their quality is the number that have survived and are still in regular use.

BSA, England, 1906-

- BSA, the Birmingham Small Arms Company Ltd, produced its first motorcycle in 1910.
- BSA ceased production in 1971 but in the late 1970s a reconstructed BSA Co. Ltd started manufacturing. Most of this company's motorcycles are supplied to overseas countries.
- BSA came into prominence and mass-market production in 1921 when they brought out their first side valve V-twin.

1918 BSA 4hp Combination Motorcycle.
£2,800-3,200 *S*

1927 BSA 500cc Motorcycle and Sidecar.
£4,000-4,500 *VER*

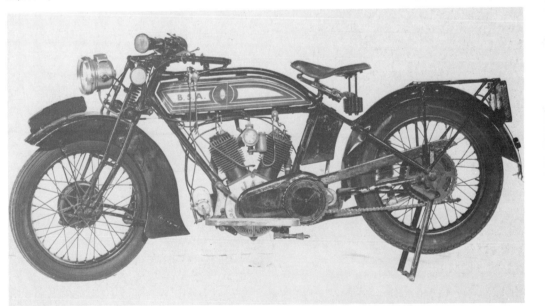

1925 BSA 986cc Motorcycle, original condition with original log book.
Est. £3,000-4,000 *MSL*

1924 BSA 500cc Solo Motorcycle, single cylinder.
£2,400-2,600 *ADT*

This particular machine is one of the later 498cc side valve models dating from 1924. It has a correctly lined flat tank, a black enamelled frame and black mudguards.

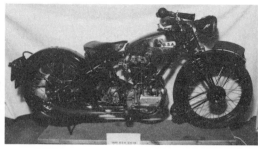

1930 BSA S30 - 19 'Light'
4.93hp 500cc Motorcycle.
£3,800-4,200 *NWB*

1924 BSA 557cc Motorcycle,
belt drive.
£2,500-3,000 *HOLL*

1935 BSA B2 250cc Motorcycle.
£2,100-2,600 *S*

During the 1930s, BSA offered a
range of 250 class machines in
side valve and overhead valve
form to appeal to all elements of
the market: the B1 side valve, B2
3-speed overhead valve, the B3 a
de luxe version of the B2 with a 4-
speed foot operated gearbox and
the B18 light featuring a hand-
operated gearbox.
This example is a B2 3-speed
model with the overhead valve
engine. It represents the middle
machine in the 250 range.

1937 BSA B20 250cc
Motorcycle.
£250-450 *S*

The frame number of this
pre-war machine indicates that it
started life as a B20 Touring
model with 250cc side valve
engine. It is now fitted with a B21
overhead valve engine from the
Sports model and is, therefore, a
potentially more exciting bike.

1937 BSA B20 250cc
Motorcycle, black with green
petrol tank.
£750-1,000 *S*

c1940 BSA M20 WD 500cc Motorcycle.
£600-900 *S*

Supplied in large numbers to British and Commonwealth forces during WWII, BSA's side valve M20 motorcycle proved to be both durable and easily maintained in the field. This example has been converted to civilian trim.

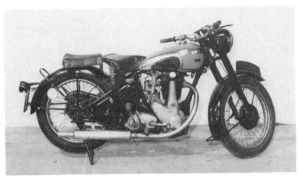

1948 BSA B33 500cc Motorcycle.
£1,300-1,600 *S*

Typical of BSA's early post-war models, the overhead valve B33 shared many components with its smaller brother, the B31, and the M series side valve models.

1952 BSA Bantam D1 125cc Motorcycle, traditional green livery.
£300-400 *S*

One of the most successful motorcycles of all time, the Bantam was in fact a copy of the pre-war DKW. This model is seen as an ideal 'first classic', thanks to a ready supply of spares and its low cost.

c1940 BSA M20 EX-WD 500cc Motorcycle.
£900-1,100 *S*

Recently imported, this machine started life as a military bike but is now painted black.

1954 BSA ZB31 350cc Motorcycle.
£1,000-1,250 *S*

1954 BSA Bantam 125cc Motorcycle.
£550-650 *S*

**1954 BSA Gold Star 500cc
Motorcycle,** in Clubman trim,
fully restored and documented.
£5,800-6,200 *RJ*

**1952 BSA Star Twin A7 500cc
Motorcycle**, unrestored.
£1,000-1,800 *CMM*

*Introduced after WWII, the 500cc
Star Twin was BSA's response to
the incredibly successful Triumph
5T Speed Twin. It was developed
throughout the 1950s into
sporting and touring models of
both 500 and 650cc's.*

**1954 BSA B31 350cc Solo
Motorcycle.**
£1,900-2,200 *ALC*

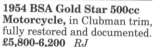

**1955 BSA D3 Bantam Major
150cc Motorcycle,** light green
and cream.
£500-700 *S*

*The success of the D1 125cc
Bantam prompted BSA to
introduce the larger D3 150cc
version in 1954.*

Locate the Source

***The source of each
illustration in Miller's
can be found by checking
the code letters below
each caption with the
key to illustrations.***

**1956 BSA DB32 Gold Star
350cc Motorcycle.**
£3,500-4,500 *S*

*The smaller of the competition
inspired Goldies, this model, like
the 500cc version, was offered in
trials, scrambles, touring and
clubman versions, with the
differences in specification being
dictated by the role intended.*

1956 BSA A1O Gold Flash 650cc Motorcycle.
£3,300-3,700 *VER*

A developed and enlarged version of the A7 500cc twin, the A1O 650cc Gold Flash is regarded by many as being one of the better A1O models, owing to its flexible and smooth power delivery.

1956 BSA B31 350cc Motorcycle, well maintained.
£1,500-1,800 *HOLL*

1956 BSA C12 250cc Motorcycle.
£350-750 *NAC*

1957 BSA M21 600cc Motorcycle.
£1,800-2,000 *S*

1957 BSA C12 250cc Motorcycle.
£1,100-1,400 *BARC*

BSA's last 250 pre-unit. Max speed 65mph.

1958 BSA Bantam D1 125cc Motorcycle.
£300-400 *S*

BSA's Bantam model in 125cc form was to remain in production from 1948-63 with very little change thanks partly to regular contracts from the Post Office. By 1958 the original version had been discontinued in favour of the plunger variant, and the machines were offered in a choice of mist green or black with cream tank panels.

1960 BSA DB Gold Star 350cc Motorcycle.
Est. £5,000-6,000 *S*

1958 BSA A10 Super Road Rocket Motorcycle.
£1,200-1,400 *S*

The BSA Super Rocket succeeded the Road Rocket in 1958 and remained in production until 1963. It featured BSA's well tried 646cc engine but with increased power output from a raised compression ratio and modified inlet and exhaust tracts. Improved braking coped with the improved performance from the new 43bhp engine and the new bike in 1958 sold for £238.3s.8d.

1959 BSA 500cc DBD 34 Gold Star Motorcycle.
£5,000-9,000 *LWH*

1960 BSA C12 250cc Motorcycle.
£200-300 *S*

1959 BSA A7SS 500cc Motorcycle.
£1,800-2,500 *BOC*
Fitted with the Britie A-S valve.

1961 BSA D1 Bantam, 125cc Motorcycle.
£700-900 *VER*

1962 BSA C15 250cc Motorcycle.
Est. £600-800 *S*

1968 BSA B44 Victor 441cc Motorcycle.
Est. £1,400-1,600 *S*

**1968 BSA US Model A65L
Spitfire MkIV Solo
Motorcycle,** lightening engine,
vertical twin, air cooled, overhead
valve, 4 stroke, 75mm bore, 74mm
stroke, 4-speed gearbox, chain
final drive, telescopic front forks,
Armstrong pivoted fork rear
suspension.
£2,800-3,200 *OxM*

1962 BSA Bantam D1 125cc Motorcycle.
£250-350 *S*

**1970 BSA A65T 650cc Thunderbolt
Motorcycle.**
Est. £1,700-2,300 *S*

1971 BSA A65 Firebird 654cc Scrambler Motorcycle.
Est. £4,250-5,250 *S*

Aimed at the US market, the Firebird was offered as a high performance 'street scrambler' variant of BSA's well proven A65 range.

1969 BSA Bantam 175cc Motorcycle.
£200-300 *S*

1971 BSA B25 Fleetstar 250cc Motorcycle.
£800-1,200 *BOC*

An ex-police motorcycle, one of 10 supplied by Peter Hammonds of Cirencester to the Gloucestershire force. Developed from the B25 Starfire, the Fleetstar, as its name suggests, was aimed at fleet users, such as the police, despatch companies and the post office.

1972 BSA Firebird 650cc Motorcycle, rebuilt 1988.
£1,500-2,000 *BOC*
This motorcycle has a rarity value as not many were sold as they were unpopular.

1988 BSA Victor/Rickman 441cc Solo Motorcycle, BSA Victor engine, Rickman Metise frame, vertical single, air cooled, overhead valve, 4 stroke, 67mm bore, 70mm stroke, 4-speed gearbox, chain final drive, Marzochi telescopic front forks, Girling pivoted fork rear suspension, hand built on/off road special.
£1,800-2,600 *OxM*

1972 BSA Rocket 3 750cc Motorcycle.
£3,500-4,000 *VER*

The Rocket 3 proved to be an excellent machine both in road use and in the field of road racing.

CALTHORPE

1921 Calthorpe 150cc Solo Motorcycle.
£800-1,000 *S*

The first Calthorpe to emerge from George Hands Birmingham factory took to the road in 1911, the company going on to produce a wide range of mainly lightweight machines using proprietary engines from Villiers, Precision, JAP and Blackburne.

1928 Calthorpe 348cc Motorcycle.
£800-1,000 *S*

The Calthorpe concern became best known with the introduction of the Ivory Calthorpe in 1929, so named because of its striking colour.

COTTON

1935 Cotton 750cc Motorcycle.
£3,300-3,900 *S*

Although one of the smaller manufacturers, Cotton met with considerable success in pre-war competition, especially in the TT in the hands of Stanley Woods, which combined with their reputation for excellent handling, attributed to the firm's distinctive straight tubed frame construction, ensured their survival through the depression years.
This 1935 model features a 750cc JAP side valve V-twin and 4-speed gearbox.

COVENTRY

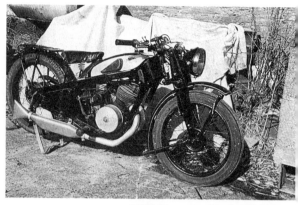

Miller's is a price GUIDE not a price LIST

1934 Coventry Eagle K2 250cc Motorcycle.
£950-1,100 *S*

The difficult trading conditions of the 1930s saw many manufacturers turn to lightweight production in order to survive. Coventry Eagle's models in this category were notable for their use of a pressed steel channel frame as seen on this example of a K2 Silent Superb 250cc.

DANDY

c1980 Dandy Miniature Motorcycle, red and white livery.
£600-700 *S*

The Japanese built Dandy featured a 2 stroke petrol engine, pull start, centrifugal clutch and chain drive. Sporting cast aluminium wheels, chunky 300 x 4 tyres and racing fairings complete the outfit.

DMW

1965 DMW Deemster 250cc Motorcycle.
Est. £500-800 *S*

Produced by the Sedgley based DMW company and utilising the Villiers 2T twin, the Deemster, an interesting mix of motorcycle and scooter, was used almost exclusively by the police for rural patrol duties.

1955 Ariel Model VH 500cc Red Hunter Motorcycle, with single cylinder overhead valve engine, in road-going form, telescopic forks, posi-stop gearbox and sprung frame with original fitted dual seat, in original condition, replaced horn, electrics functioning, in running order.
£1,600-1,800 *S*

1927 AJS Model H6 350cc Motorcycle, overhead valve.
£4,000-6,000 *PC*

This model was commonly called a Big Port due to the large exhaust pipe, however, the earlier 1924-5 models were larger still. They were extremely lightweight and performed well enough to be raced when stripped down. In road form they could achieve 75mph.

1912 Abingdon King Dick 3hp Motorcycle.
£7,500-8,500 *S*

1952 AJS 7R 350cc Motorcycle, overhead valve.
£11,000-15,000 *VER*

1977 Benelli 750 Sei Motorcycle, 6 cylinders, in road going form, 539 miles recorded, in excellent condition throughout.
Est. £3,500-3,800 *S*

This motorcycle was recently imported from the US where it was kept in storage since its manufacture.

The engine detail of the **1977 Benelli 750 Sei Motorcycle.**

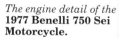

1912 Bradbury 500cc Motorcycle and Sidecar.
£7,000-7,500 *VER*

1920 Beardmore Precision 350cc Motorcycle, 2 stroke.
£4,750-5,250 *VER*

1959 BMW R69 600cc Motorcycle, painted black, good condition.
Est. £3,500-4,000 *S*

Introduced to the British market in 1956, weighing 444lbs, it was the most expensive machine in the BMW range on the British market in 1959. This motorcycle differs slightly from factory specification in having alloy rims and a non-standard front brake.

1938 Brough Superior SS100 Motorcycle, twin overhead valve, Matchless engine, restored to concours condition.
Est. £22,000-26,000 *S*

'A luxury machine with an out of the ordinary performance' reported Motor Cycling magazine after road testing in 1938. Factory records show this bike as '1938 Demo. SS100 x Laird. Spring Wheel', and records the date of despatch as 4th March 1938.

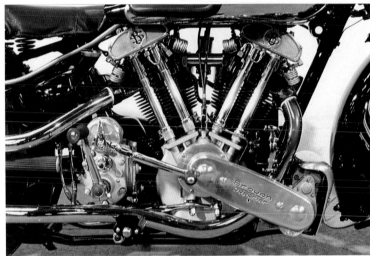

Detail of the engine of
1938 Brough Superior SS100 Motorcycle.

1953 BSA C11 250cc Motorcycle.
£1,000-1,500 *VER*

1949 BSA Bantam D1 125cc Motorcycle, rebuilt.
£700-800 *S*

This motorcycle made its first appearance in 1948. It was to be adopted by Police Forces and the Post Office and was used by amateur riders with some success in competition.

1968 BSA Bantam D14/4 Sports 175cc Motorcycle,
£300-500 *BOC*

1963 BSA B40 350cc Motorcycle,
£800-1,200 *BOC*

BSA's are on the whole solid, reliable and reasonably priced motorcycles. The spares availability is excellent.

1955 BSA Golden Flash Motorcycle, with its original Watsonian sidecar, concours condition.
£4,000-5,000 *DG*

1964 BSA Café Racer A65L 650cc Solo Motorcycle, vertical twin, air-cooled, overhead valve, 4 stroke engine, 4 speed gearbox, chain final drive, telescopic front forks, pivoted fork rear suspension by Girling, hand-built special.
£1,600-2,000 *OxM*

1988 NorBSA Café Racer A65L 650cc Solo Motorcycle, Norton featherbed vertical twin, air-cooled, overhead valve, 4 stroke engine, 4 speed gearbox, chain final drive, Norton roadholder telescopic front forks, pivoted fork rear suspension, Marzocchi hand-built special.
£3,000-3,500 *OxM*

1990 BSA AI0 Café Racer 650cc Solo Motorcycle, vertical twin, air-cooled, overhead valve, 4 stroke engine, 4 speed BSA gearbox, chain final drive, BSA telescopic front forks, Girling pivoted fork rear suspension, hand-built special.
£2,300-2,800 *OxM*

1970 BSA Thunderbolt A65 650cc Motorcycle.
£1,700-2,000 *S*

1964 Cotton Telstar MKII 247cc Racing Motorcycle.
£1,700-2,000 *S*

**c1925 Excelsior 250cc
Motorcycle,** countershaft
gearbox, twin port engine,
finished in red and black,
fitted with a period
acetylene lighting set, very
good condition.
Est. £1,400-1,600 *S*

*Excelsior became involved
in Motorcycles in 1896 and
up to the 1930s offered an
extensive range of machines
powered by engines from
Villiers, Blackburne and
JAP.*

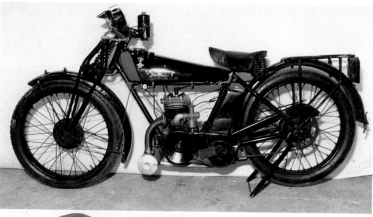

**1988 Ducati Saxon-Brancato
350R Motorcycle.
£7,000-8,000** *DOC*

*This model has been
manufactured since 1971 but the
design remains unchanged.*

**1920 Douglas 4hp
Twin Cylinder
Motorcycle.
£3,300-3,700** *VER*

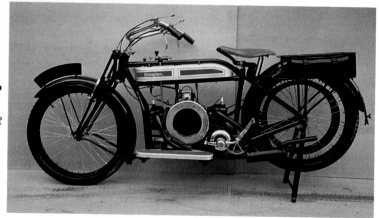

**1974 Ducati Desmo
750cc Motorcycle.
Est. £3,000-3,500** *S*

1989 Harley-Davidson Sportster 1200cc Motorcycle.
£3,500-4,500 *HDOC*

1970 Honda CB 750 736cc Motorcycle, transverse 4 cylinder overhead camshaft engine, 5 speed gearbox, good condition.
£7,000-9,000 *S*

This machine was recently imported into the UK from the USA.

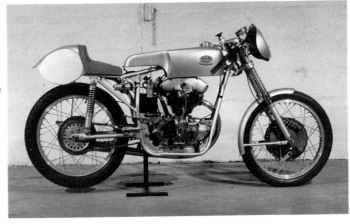

1955 FB Mondial 125cc Bialbero Racing Motorcycle.
Est. £12,000-13,000 *S*

1924 Francis Barnett 1½hp Motorcycle, with original flywheel magneto ignition and hand-operated gear change.
£500-700 *S*

Francis Barnett commenced motorcycle production in Coventry in 1919.

1921 Ivy 224cc Motorcycle, finished in green and black, fitted with footboards, carrier, front and rear lamps and a bulb horn, good condition throughout.
£1,500-2,000 *S*

Ivy were one of the first exponents of the 2 stroke motorcycle offering machines in the pre-WWI era of 225cc and 296cc, supplemented in 1919 with outside flywheel engines of 246cc. They won their class in the 1921 500 miles race at Brooklands. This example was first registered on 10.3.21.

1950 James Comet 98cc Motorcycle.
£150-550 *NAC*

1927 Humber 350cc Motorcycle, recorded 700 miles from new, original condition throughout, with dating letter, toolkit, instruction book and well documented history.
£3,500-4,000 *S*

1913 Indian 1000cc Motorcycle, 2 speed and V-twin cylinder.
£15,500-17,500 *VER*

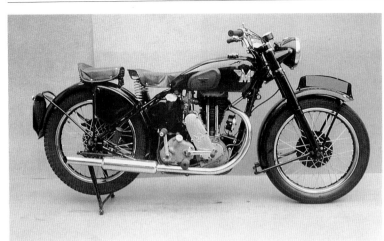

1948 Matchless Model G3L 350cc Motorcycle.
£2,200-2,600 *VER*

1957 Matchless G3LS 350cc Motorcycle, overhead valve, 4 stroke.
£2,000-2,500 *ROB*

1957 Maico Taifun 400cc Motorcycle, twin cylinder 2 stroke, concours condition.
£4,500-5,000 *MOC*

Only 40 machines were imported into the UK between 1954 to 1958. This very advanced design was first manufactured in Germany in 1953. Classic Bike Show Award Winner.

1953 Matchless G3LC 350cc Solo Motorcycle, 11,000 miles from new, original engine, fully restored body.
£1,700-2,000 *ALC*

**1957 Norton Manx 350cc
Motorcycle,** overhead camshaft.
£10,000-11,000 *VER*

1953 Moto Guzzi Falcone Sport 500cc Motorcycle,
restored 5 years ago, unused since.
Est. £4,500-4,800 *S*

*Originally introduced in 1950, the Falcone was to remain in
production until 1967, mainly at the behest of the Italian police
and services. For much of its production life, it was available
in either Tourismo or Sport variants as offered here. Despite
their almost vintage looks, the machines offered a good level of
performance and handling.*

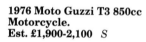

**1976 Moto Guzzi T3 850cc
Motorcycle.
Est. £1,900-2,100** *S*

1936 Norton 350cc Motorcycle,
overhead camshaft.
£19,000-21,000 *CM*

*Purchased then taken to South Africa
where it was raced but returned to the
Norton factory each year to be
updated and modified. This
motorcycle won Racing Bike of the
Bristol Show 1990 and 1991.*

1959 Norton Jubilee 250cc Motorcycle.
£1,500-2,000 *NOC*

1963 Norton Dominator 88SS 500cc Motorcycle.
£3,000-3,500 *VER*

1971 Norton Commando Fastback 750cc Motorcycle.
£5,000-6,000 *NOC*

This Motorcycle was exported to America in 1971 which explains the high handlebars.

1988 BVR Norton Café Racer 1,000cc Solo Motorcycle, Brian Valentine Racing S104 engine, Norton featherbed wideline frame, V-twin, air-cooled, overhead valve, 4 stroke, 4 speed Harley-Davidson gearbox, chain final drive, Norton roadholder telescopic front forks, pivoted fork rear suspension, hand-built special.
£4,500-5,500 *OxM*

**1958 Raleigh MkI 49cc
Moped,** unrestored.
£50-100 *RSS*

1914 Overseas 490cc Motorcycle Combination, fitted
with basket sidecar, restored, Pioneer registered.
Est. £6,000-7,000 *S*

*Built by the Overseas Motor Company, Birmingham, the
Overseas motorcycle was offered in either single or V-twin
form from 1909 to 1916 and offered mainly for the British
Colonial market.*

*Originally produced under the P & M name, after their designers Phelon and Moore, Panther was
one of the longest established producers of motorcycles in Britain, having entered production in 1900.
During the 1930s Panther introduced the Red Panther range of machines which offered excellent
value at low cost, thus ensuring the company's survival.*

*This example of the Model 85 is fitted with a 498cc model 50 engine, which features Panther's
forward sloping cylinder, a characteristic to be found on virtually every large capacity machine
produced by the company.*

*Panther remained in production into the 1960s, although in receivership, but the dramatic decline in
their staple sidecar market forced them to cease production in 1964.*

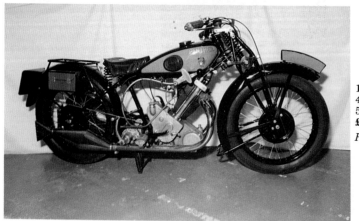

**1930 Panther Model 85
498cc Motorcycle,** with model
50 engine.
£2,000-2,500 *CMM*
Restoration not complete.

1956 Reliant Regal Mk II 747cc.
£1,000-1,500 *RSS*

1968 Raleigh RM6 49cc
Moped.
£50-100 *RSS*

1923 Raleigh 2¾hp Motorcycle,
showing engine detail.
£3,800-4,000 *S*

Raleigh motorcycles were built initially up to 1906 and then again from 1919 to 1934. By the 1920s the machines were largely conventional in design, and used gearboxes and engines by Sturmey-Archer, who formed part of the Raleigh group. The 2¾ hp featured a side-valve single cylinder engine and countershaft gearbox and a high level of build quality.

Raleigh returned to powered, two-wheel production after WWII with a series of mopeds.

1905 Rexette 7hp Forcar.
£12,000-13,000 *VER*

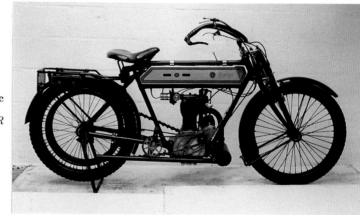

1911 Rudge 500cc Motorcycle.
£5,000-6,000 *VER*

1934 Scott Flyer 596cc 'Clubman Special' Solo Motorcycle, Webb front forks, 21in front wheel, throttle control oil pump, restored.
£3,500-4,500 *ALC*

1939 Royal Enfield Model KX 1140cc Motorcycle and Sidecar, side valve V-twin engine, Albion 4 speed gearbox, restored.
Est. £3,500-4,200 *S*

1937 Rudge Rapid 250cc Motorcycle.
Est. £1,800-2,200 *S*

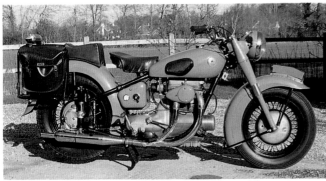

1954 Sunbeam S7 Motorcycle, original condition.
£2,500-3,500 *DG*

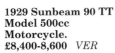

1929 Sunbeam 90 TT Model 500cc Motorcycle.
£8,400-8,600 *VER*

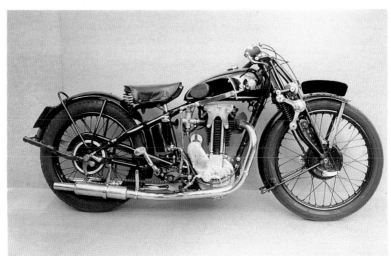

1985 Suzuki RG 500cc Motorcycle, 2 stroke, 6 speed gearbox, Deca piston brakes.
£2,000-2,500 *ROB*

c1927 Sunbeam Model I 2¾hp Motorcycle.
£2,900-3,100 *S*

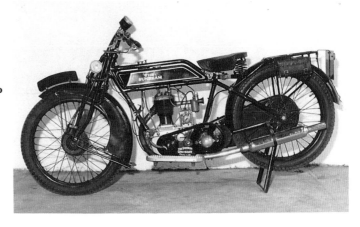

1982 Suzuki GSX 1000 SZ Katana 997cc Motorcycle, transverse 4 cylinder overhead camshaft, 5 speed gearbox, chain final drive, condition as new.
Est. £6,000-7,000 *S*

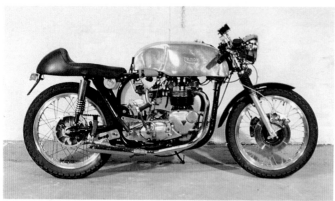

c1960 Triton 750cc Motorcycle.
Est. £2,000-2,500 *S*

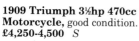

1909 Triumph 3½hp 470cc Motorcycle, good condition.
£4,250-4,500 *S*

1914 Triumph 500cc Motorcycle.
£5,000-6,000 *VER*

DOUGLAS, England, 1907-56

- The first Douglas motorcycle was designed by J.F. Barter. It had 2.5hp and was identical to Barter's Fairy (Fee) motorcycles.
- Douglas supplied many 348cc models to the forces during WWI.
- Douglas manufactured the first special dirt-track racing motorcycles (496cc and 596cc) in 1928.
- The Douglas family relinquished control of the factory in 1932.

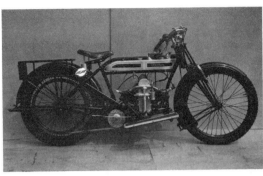

1921 Douglas 2¾hp Motorcycle.
£4,500-5,500 *VER*

Developed from the WWI model, the little fore and aft Dougie twin remained popular during the 1920s thanks to its ease of handling and good performance.

1920 Douglas 4hp Solo Motorcycle.
£2,200-2,400 *S*

Douglas introduced the 4hp in 1915 in the midst of hostilities, Walter Moore designing what was effectively a 'squish' head design of combustion chamber to achieve maximum power for this new machine. The 595cc engine proved dependable in military service, generally with sidecar attachment, and saw service as senior personnel transport and also as transport for mobile wireless transmitters. The 4hp featured a 3 speed countershaft gearbox, and claimed petrol consumption of 75-80mpg.

1952 Douglas Mark IV 350cc Motorcycle.
£800-900 *S*

Post-war Douglas motorcycles adopted the horizontally opposed twin, instead of the previous fore and aft layout. While enhancing engine cooling, this design left the cylinders in an exposed position.

Miller's is a price GUIDE not a price LIST

1926 Douglas EW 26 350cc Solo Motorcycle.
£850-1,050 *S*

1929 Douglas Model EW B29 350cc Motorcycle.
Est. £2,800-3,500 *S*

The new model EW appeared in 1926, the 348cc engine developing 10bhp. The new engine featured aluminium pistons and had totally enclosed valve gear and the efficient Douglas Low Pressure Braking System.

1929 Douglas Model D29 350cc Motorcycle.
£2,700-3,700 *S*

Developed from the 2¾hp model, the D28 and D29 models were only produced in 1928 and 1929.

**1935 Douglas 500cc
Motorcycle.
£1,500-2,000** *P*

DUCATI

**1978 Ducati 500GTL 497cc 2
Cylinder Motorcycle.
£2,200-2,700** *COYS*

*Ducati's range of parallel twins,
introduced in the 1970s, never met
with the same popularity enjoyed
by the company's singles and V- twins.*

**1975 Ducati 500GTL 497cc 2
Cylinder Motorcycle.
£1,500-2,000** *COYS*

**1977 Ducati 900cc Motorcycle.
£4,500-5,500** *VER*

Ducati has always been famed for both its racing and road-going motorcycles, more often than not powered by its own twin cylinder engines using the company's famed desmodromic valve gear designed by Fabio Taglioni. The company has traditionally offered road-going versions of its most successful racing bikes, one of the most recent of which was the 851 Superbike, commemorating Franco Lucianelli's victory in the Probike Championship aboard an 851.

1989 Ducati V-twin 851cc Superbike, with red, white and green racing livery.
£4,500-5,500 *COYS*

> **Miller's is a price GUIDE not a price LIST**

Ducati 160 Junior 160cc Motorcycle.
£200-300 *S*

EMC PUCH

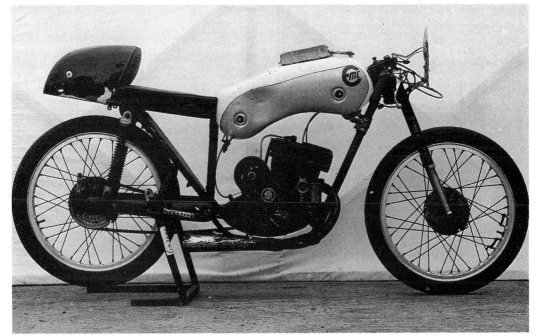

EMC Puch 125cc Motorcycle.
Est. £6,000-8,000 *P*

This motorcycle was owned by Mr Griffiths, the famous pre-war racer, and kept by him in the Stanford Hall Museum.

EXCELSIOR

**1934 Excelsior 148cc
Motorcycle.
£800-1,200** *S*

*Although best remembered for the
Manxman, Excelsior, like many of
their competitors, were reliant on
a range of cheap Villiers 2-strokes
to see them through the depression
years.*

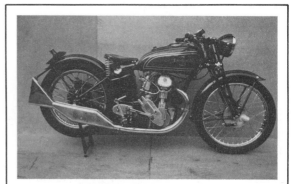

**1936 Excelsior Manxman
250cc Motorcycle.
£8,000-9,000** *VER*

*Numerous successes on the
racetrack helped sales of these
handsome machines.*

**1936 Excelsior Solo Racing
Motorcycle.
£3,500-4,500** *S*

*This machine is thought to be the
example that won the 1952 Isle of
Man Southern 100 in the hands of
Bill Smith.*

**Excelsior Talismara Twin
250cc 2-Stroke Motorcycle.
Est. £1,350-1,750** *P*

**1936 Excelsior Manxman
Special Motorcycle.
£3,000-3,500** *S*

*One of the great machines of the
1930s the Excelsior Manxman
featured an overhead cam single
cylinder engine that was at the
forefront of motorcycle technology.*

FRANCIS BARNETT

1939 Francis Barnett Cruiser 250cc Motorcycle.
£400-600 *S*

The 1930s saw an increasing number of machines being 'enclosed' in an attempt to make them more 'user friendly' (i.e. keeping the rider clean), one of the most notable exponents being Francis Barnett with their series of Cruisers.

1959 Francis Barnett Falcon 81 197cc Motorcycle.
£200-300 *S*

Francis Barnett offered a range of reliable commuting machines to the public in the post-war years of which the Falcon 81 was a good example, featuring a Villiers 10E 2-stroke engine, coupled to a 3-speed gearbox, a fully sprung frame, and attractive styling.

1955 Francis Barnett Falcon 74 197cc Motorcycle.
£350-450 *S*

GILERA

1960 Francis Barnett Falcon 87 199cc Motorcycle.
£200-450 *S*

Introduced in 1960, the Falcon 87 featured the new AMC built 199cc engine in cycle parts similar to those of the model that it replaced, the Falcon 81.

1952 Gilera Saturno 500cc Motorcycle.
Est. £3,500-4,000 *S*

With a history of motorcycle manufacture going back to 1909 Gilera focused their attention on sporting machines, and Giuseppe Gilera himself was to be a successful and competitive rider of his own machines.

Gilera Giubileo 98cc 4 stroke Motorcycle, in red.
Est. £400-800 *P*

Gilera produced motorcycles first in 1969 and are producing them today under the Piaggio Group.

HARLEY-DAVIDSON, America, 1903-

- Founded by William A. Davidson, Walter Davidson Snr, Arthur Davidson, and William S. Harley in Milwaukee, Wisconsin.
- The first 3 motorcycles were virtually hand-made. Demand soon exceeded supply, and in 1906 the company produced 50 machines.
- In 1907, Harley-Davidson Inc. was formed and production moved to the present Juneau Avenue address.
- During WWI, some 20,000 motorcycles saw active service. However, no less than 90,000 bikes were used during WWII, the vast majority of them WLA V-twins.
- In the 1960s, Harley-Davidson bought the Italian company Aermacchi, where new models - including 49cc mopeds - came into production.
- In 1965, the legendary FLH Electra Glide was launched.
- In 1984, Harley-Davidson launched the Softail, followed the next year by the Heritage version.
- The future of Harley-Davidson Inc. was secured in 1986 when the company was floated on the New York Stock Exchange.

1915 Harley-Davidson 11hp Motorcycle and Sidecar.
£650-1,000 *P*

1954 Harley-Davidson FLH Hydra Glide, 1207cc Motorcycle.
£12,000-20,000 *HDOC*

Fairly rare, Harley-Davidson made just over 2,000 of the 50th Anniversary Special.

1964 Harley-Davidson 'P' Servicar, 750cc Motorcycle.
£8,000-10,000 *HDOC*

In production from 1932 to 1972. Very few modifications were introduced over that period. The Servicar saw extensive use by US police forces as repair tenders to their motorcycle fleets.

1981 Harley-Davidson FLTC 1340cc Classic Electra Glide Motorcycle.
£9,000-10,000 *S*

1984 Harley-Davidson FLHTC Classic Electra Glide 1340cc Motorcycle.
Est. £5,800-6,200 *S*

The FLHTC Classic features the 1340cc evolution engine and 5-speed gearbox in full dress touring package including the handlebar mounted half-fairing, top box, panniers, footboards, king and queen seat, etc. to create a true grand tourer.

1988 Harley-Davidson Wide Glide Softail 1340cc Motorcycle.
£6,000-6,500 *HDOC*

Locate the Source

The source of each illustration in Miller's can be found by checking the code letters below each caption with the list of contributors.

1989 Harley-Davidson 'D' FXR Pursuit Glide 1340cc Motorcycle.
£6,000-6,500 *HDOC*

HARRIS

Harris Magnum One 1198cc Motorcycle.
£3,500-4,000 *SS*

During the 1970s, Japanese engine technology far outstripped that of their chassis, resulting in some interesting handling characteristics. As a consequence, frame builders such as Harris started to produce frames for a variety of engines. The company now competes regularly in Grand Prix with motorcycles fitted with Japanese engines.

1983 Harris Magnum Two 120hp 1085cc Motorcycle.
£3,500-4,000 *SS*

HEALEY

1976 Healey 1000/4 997cc Motorcycle.
Est. £11,000-12,000 *S*

The Healey built between 1973-76 in limited numbers featured a developed and refined version of Ariel's Square Four engine installed in a tubular spine frame.

HESKETH

1984 Hesketh V1000 Motorcycle.
Est. £4,000-5,000 *S*

HONDA, Japan, 1948-

- Soichiro Honda founded the Honda Motor Company in 1948 and the fame of the company is now worldwide.
- Between 1948 and 1954, Honda steadily increased the number of new designs and by 1960, over 50 countries had imported in excess of 160,000 motorcycles.
- Racing played a large role in Honda's life during the 1950s and 1960s when riders such as Jim Redman, Luigi Taveri and Mike Hailwood, among others, were both winning and creating new records.
- Honda's current list of motorcycles ranges from 48cc to 1085cc models.

1962 Honda C72 250cc Motorcycle.
£300-400 *S*

1962 Honda C92 125cc Motorcycle.
£500-750 *S*

1963 Honda CB77 Super Sport Motorcycle.
Est. £2,000-2,500 *S*

1964 Honda CB92 Benly Super Sport 124.7cc Motorcycle.
£2,500-2,800 *S*

1968 Honda 49cc 'Monkey Bike'.
£1,200-1,800 *S*

One of the Honda Company's more eccentric models, the 'Monkey' bikes became fashionable as paddock transport and tenders to yachts, as well as being greeted with delight by those youngsters who were affluent or persuasive enough to acquire one.

1969 Honda CB750 KO Motorcycle.
£6,500-7,500 *S*

1969/70 Honda CB750 Motorcycle.
Est. £4,000-5,000 *S*

The first of the superbikes, Honda's CB750 took the world market by storm in 1968, introducing a performance and a luxury that had previously been unheard of.

1964 Honda CB77 305cc Motorcycle.
Est. £1,700-2,000 *S*

1972 Honda CB750 K2 Motorcycle.
Est. £2,800-3,500 *LF*

1973 Honda Dunstall 900cc Motorcycle.
Est. £2,800-3,200 *S*

This example of a Paul Dunstall equipped Honda CB750 features the full and distinctive fibreglass body package including a full fairing, rear set and clip-ons. The engine is fitted with a big bore conversion, increasing capacity to 900cc, whilst close ratio gears aid transmission. Larger front discs and an upgraded suspension set-up help to keep things under control on what is almost a race bike in disguise.

Miller's is a price **GUIDE** not a price **LIST**

1976 Honda CB750F Super Sport Motorcycle.
Est. £1,700-2,200 *S*

Introduced in 1975, the CB750F was an attempt to recapture some of the ground lost to their competitors in the super-bike market, notably Kawasaki. Featuring revised styling, a four-into-one exhaust system and a rear disc brake, along with a power output raised to compensate for the erosions made since 1968 due to emission controls, the machine answered its brief, looking lighter and sportier than its 'four pipe' touring 'K' brothers, with performance that matched many of its rivals.

1976 Honda CB250 G5 Motorcycle.
Est. £800-1,200 *LF*

1974 Honda XL250 Motorcycle.
Est. £1,200-1,400 *S*

1982 Honda Goldwing GL1100 Motorcycle.
Est. £2,000-2,500 *LF*

Following on from the GL1000 Goldwing, the GL1100 offered more performance and a greater range of accessories.

1977 Honda Goldwing GL 1000 Motorcycle.
Est. £1,000-1,500 *LF*

The 999cc water cooled Honda Goldwing GL 1000 was introduced in 1975/76 and created an absolute sensation. The transverse mounted double overhead camshaft engine has four horizontal cylinders, two on each side. The machine produces 80bhp at 7000rpm, and the earlier models are perhaps cleaner of line than the later examples. Despite the massive size of these bikes they are capable of 125mph.

1987 Honda CBXC1000 Motorcycle.
Est. £4,000-4,500 *LF*

Honda RS 125W 1980C
Motorcycle.
Est. £700-900 *P*

**1981 Honda CB1100 RB
Motorcycle.
Est. £4,000-5,000** *LF*

*Derived from Honda's world
endurance championship
machines, the CB1100 RB was
special in that only 1100
motorcycles were produced. At the
time of its introduction, this road
legal racer redefined superbike
performance parameters.*

**1988 Honda Goldwing 1200cc
Motorcycle.
£6,000-8,000** *GOC*

**1982 Honda Goldwing GL1100
DXC 83hp 1085cc Motorcycle.
£3,500-4,000** *GOC*

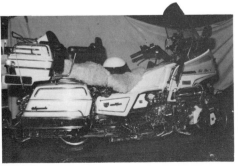

**1988 Honda Modern Tourer
Goldwing Aspencade 1200cc
Motorcycle.
£8,500-10,000** *GOC*

Honda CB92 Benly Super Sport 125cc Motorcycle.
£1,700-1,900 *S*

Honda CB250 Motorcycle.
£100-200 *MSL*

H.R.D.

1935 H.R.D. Comet 500cc Motorcycle.
£5,500-6,500 *VER*

1927 Humber 350cc Motorcycle.
Est. £3,000-3,500 *S*

HUMBER

Introduced in 1923, the 2¾hp side valve model with engine dimensions of 75mm x 79mm, and 3-speed gearbox was to continue in production in developed form until 1930 when Humber ceased motorcycle production.

1912 Humber 500cc Motorcycle.
£7,000-8,000 *S*

The machine is started by inserting the starting handle into the hub when the machine is up on its rear stand, and the gearing is controlled by pedals from the footboard. It has a Pioneer Certificate No. 278 issued on the 13th February 1955.

1924 Humber 2¾hp 349cc Motorcycle.
£1,500-2,000 *S*

HUSQVARNA

c1970 Husqvarna 500cc Motocross Motorcycle.
£400-600 *S*

INDIAN

1913 Indian 7hp single speed 1000cc Motorcycle.
£8,000-10,000 unrestored
£15,000-18,000 restored *IMC*

It is very difficult to find parts for such a high quality, large capacity 'Pioneer'.

1946 Indian Chief 74 cu in 1200cc Motorcycle.
£10,000-12,000 *IMC*

Indian was Harley-Davidson's main competitor in the United States until the 1950s. Indian produced typically American machines which offered high levels of torque and comfort suited to the long distances which can be covered in America. The company is now being revived and prototypes in the traditional mould have been shown in America.

IVY

1921 Ivy 224cc Motorcycle.
£1,500-2,000 *S*

The Ivy Company was one of the first exponents of the 2 stroke motorcycle offering machines in the pre-Great War era of 225cc and 296cc supplemented in 1919 with outside flywheel engines of 246cc and 346cc. They were also unusual for gaining some success at Brooklands winning their class in the 1921 500 miles race with an Ivy Three when racing was very much the preserve of the 4 stroke.

1926 Ivy 2¾hp Motorcycle.
£2,000-2,500 *S*

JAMES

1955 James 197cc 'Captain' Motorcycle.
£180-250 *S*

James, and their AMC partners Francis Barnett, produced a series of no-thrills lightweights in the post-war years utilising Villiers engines.

JAWA

1992 Jawa Model 638 350cc Motorcycle.
Est. £900-1,000

1986 Jawa 350 Motorcycle with Velorex Sidecar.
Est. £1,000-1,500 *LF*

KAWASAKI, Japan, 1949-

- Founded in 1878 as the Kawasaki Dockyard and branching into aircraft production in 1937, this old established Japanese manufacturing group built its first motorcycle at Akashi in 1949 in the redundant aircraft factory.
- This course of events was determined by the outcome of WWII, after which they were prohibited from manufacturing munitions etc.

- Late in 1960, the Kawasaki Aircraft Co. Ltd founded an assembly plant in Kobe in order to design and mass-produce motorcycles.
- In 1969, Dave Simmonds became World Champion in road racing on a Kawasaki 123cc.
- Kawasaki is now one of the leading motorcycle manufacturers in Japan.

1971 Kawasaki H1A 500cc Motorcycle.
Est. £1,200-1,300 *S*

1975 Kawasaki Z1B 903cc Motorcycle.
Est. £12,500-15,000 *S*

1981 Kawasaki Police Z1000 Motorcycle.
£2,000-3,000 *S*

KTM

c1980 KTM 250cc
Motorcross
Motorcycle.
Est. £200-250 *S*

Miller's is a price
GUIDE not a price
LIST

LEVIS

**1924 Levis Model K 2½hp
Motorcycle,** original condition.
£2,000-2,500 *S*

*Levis 2 strokes earned a
formidable reputation during the
1920s and won a TT. This
example is fitted with period
Miller front and rear acetylene
lamps and has retained all its
original control levers.*

LAVERDA

1968 Laverda 750 Motorcycle.
Est. £2,250-2,750 *P*

LMC

1914 LMC 550cc Motorcycle.
£4,000-5,000 *VER*

MAICO

1957 Maico Blizzard, concours standard.
£1,800-2,000 *MOC*

1958 Maico Mobil 200cc fully enclosed Motorcycle, restored condition, except for missing indicators and incorrect silencer.
£2,350-2,500 *MOC*

First manufactured in Germany in 1952 as 150cc, followed by a 175cc model and finally as 200cc, with single cylinder 2 stroke engine and 300 x 14in tyres. Only the later 200cc machines were imported into the UK between 1954-58.

c1970 Maico Model 501 Motorcross Motorcycle, good condition, believed to be an ex- works machine.
£800-1,000 *S*

MATCHLESS, England, 1899-1969

- This once-famous marque, based at Plumstead Road, Woolwich, fitted in the early days De Dion, JAP, MAG and MMC engines.
- Brothers Harry and Charlie Collier won the TT races in 1907, 1909 and 1910.
- H. H. Collier, the father and founder of Matchless, died in 1926, and in 1928 the company became a limited company.
- The Collier brothers bought AJS in 1931 and soon there was very little difference between the two makes.
- Matchless faded away in the 1960s following the deaths of the brothers and the financially troubled 1950s.

1952 Matchless Model G80S 500cc Motorcycle.
£2,000-2,500 *NWB*

1921 Matchless Model H 8hp Motorcycle and Sidecar, concours standard.
£6,000-7,000 *S*

Designed purely for sidecar use, the Matchless Model H featured a fully sprung frame and a 3 speed countershaft gearbox.

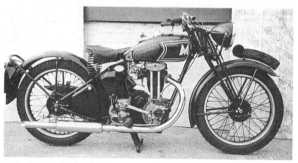

1936 Matchless G2 250cc Motorcycle.
£1,300-1,600 *S*

Introduced in 1936 the G2 featured coil ignition with a magneto sparked version, the G2M being offered as an alternative. It shared many similarities with its larger cousin, the G3.

1955 Matchless G3LS 350cc Motorcycle.
£1,000-1,300 *S*

1954 Matchless G9 500cc Motorcycle.
£700-900 *S*

A partially restored example of the 500cc Matchless G9. This motorcycle was introduced in 1948 with its AJS cousin, the Model 20, in response to the success of Triumph's 5T Speed Twin.

1954 Matchless G9 500cc.
£2,300-2,700 AMOC

1961 Matchless G12 CSR 650cc Motorcycle.
£1,800-2,100 *S*

The sporting variant of the G12 range, the CSR featured polished alloy mudguards and a slightly tuned engine.

1955 Matchless G3LS 350cc, restored, with period extras.
£1,300-2,500 NAC

1960 Matchless G12 650cc Motorcycle.
Est. £1,800-2,300 *S*

The Matchless G12, along with its cousin from AJS, was unusual in its use of 3 bearings for the crankshaft instead of the more general two.

1989 Matchless Rotax 500cc Motorcycle.
£1,200-1,600 *VER*

1987 Matchless G8O Motorcycle.
Est. £1,250-1,750 *P*

This motorcycle was one of the first 13 motorcycles made by L. F. Harris, Rushden Ltd. of Newton Abbot, Devon, who owns the rights to produce motorcycles, with the Matchless name.

MINERVA

1903 Minerva 2¼hp Motorcycle.
£5,000-6,000 *VER*

This early 'Pioneer' displays many typical characteristics, including the direct belt drive and the large rectangular fuel tank placed in the centre of what is essentially a strengthened bicycle frame. The placing of the engine in the central position was, in 1903, a relatively new innovation.

MORGAN

Morgan three-wheelers fall into a middle ground between motorcycles and cars and are readily accepted by both groups. Described by enthusiasts as the safest device on wheels, they offer, in a sporting guise, a combination of high top speed and acceleration.

1932 Morgan, JAP engine, overhead valve 1100cc Motorcycle.
£15,500-16,500 *VER*

MOTOBECANE

c1924 Motobecane Lightweight Motorcycle, in good general condition with period toolbox.
£350-450 *S*

Motobecane machines were made on the Seine in France, initially by Usines Motoconfort at Pantin, and latterly by Usines Motobecane at 53 Rue de Paris. The firm were later also responsible for the Mobylette moped made in large numbers.

MOTO GUZZI

1952 Moto Guzzi Airone Sport 250cc Motorcycle, single cylinder, overhead valve, 4 stroke, pushrod engine.
£3,000-3,500 *ROB*

1955 Moto Guzzi 192cc Motorcycle.
£7,000-8,000 *HOLL*

1952 Moto Guzzi Astore 500cc Motorcycle,
£7,800-8,200 *S*

1953 Moto Guzzi Astore 500cc Motorcycle, fitted with Hartford type friction dampers, good condition.
£2,500-3,000 *S*

1953 Moto Guzzi Airone Sport 250cc Motorcycle, unrestored.
Est. £2,300-2,800 *S*

First introduced in 1939 as a civilian bike the Airone was later also to see military service in post-war years as the Airone Militaire. The Airone Sport remained in production from 1949 to 1958, its overhead valve engine developing some 12bhp at 5200rpm.

1964 Moto Guzzi Falcone GT 500cc Motorcycle.
Est. £3,000-3,500 *S*

This machine follows the classic Moto Guzzi layout of single cylinder forward facing horizontal air cooled engine with double overhead camshaft and 4 speed gearbox. Italian machines were early in the field with sprung frames at the rear, and this example features Guzzi's own brand of damped rear suspension.

**1970 Moto Guzzi V7 750cc
Motorcycle Combination.
£1,600-1,700** *P*

**1980 Moto Guzzi V50 II 493cc
Motorcycle.
Est. £800-900** *S*

MV AGUSTA, Italy, 1946-

- MV (Meccanica Verghera) were famous helicopter manufacturers, owned by the Count Agusta family, who started producing motorcycles in 1946.
- The earliest machines to bear the name were 98cc 2 strokes aimed at providing cheap, economical transport.
- The marque is now best remembered for their legendary 4 cylinder double overhead camshaft which dominated the race tracks.
- A combination of increased orders for helicopters plus a lack of racing successes led to the gradual winding down of the company.
- Arturo Magni, who was MV Agusta's racing chief, is producing MH machines which are built on MV Agusta lines.

MOTO MORINI

**Moto Morini Strada 3½ 350cc
Motorcycle,** V-twin overhead valve engine, 5 speed gearbox, in good condition, finished in silver and black.
Est. £2,250-2,750 *P*

**c1952 MV Agusta 125cc
Lungo Motorcycle,** 2 stroke, single cylinder, bore and stroke 53 x 56mm, with compression ratio of 9.1 giving 8.5bhp at 8000rpm, 4 special gearbox, girder/blade front suspension swing arm 2 stroke rear, 2.75 tyres back and front, dry weight 95kg, restored in red and black.
Est. £2,500-3,500 *P*

**c1960 MV Agusta 149cc
Motorcycle.
Est. £500-600** *S*

c1957 MV Agusta 250cc Raid Motorcycle,
unrestored condition.
Est. £1,000-1,500 *P*

**c1969 MV Agusta Sport Drum
Brake Type 214 Motorcycle.
Est. £20,000-23,000** *P*

*The engine is a 4 cylinder air-
cooled double overhead cam of
743cc with a bore and stroke of
65 x 56mm, 9.5:1 compression
giving 65bhp at 8500rpm. The
chassis has telescopic forks,
swing arm frame, wire wheels
and alloy rims. The front tyre is
100/90 V18 the rear 110 x 90
V18. The carburettors are 4 VHB
27A Del'orto.*

**Miller's is a price
GUIDE not a price
LIST**

**1969 MV Agusta 250B 250cc
Motorcycle,** original condition.
Est. £800-1,200 *S*

**c1963 MV Agusta Turismo
150cc Motorcycle,** 4 stroke
overhead valve.
Est. £400-800 *P*

c1972 MV Agusta 350GT
Motorcycle, requires
restoration.
Est. £1,500-1,800 *P*

1976 MV Agusta 125 Sport
Motorcycle,
good condition.
Est. £1,200-1,500 *S*

NER-A-CAR

1924 Ner-a-car 285cc
Motorcycle.
£4,000-4,500 *S*

*Built under licence by Sheffield
Simplex from its American
inventor J. Neracher, the British
built examples adopted chain
drive as opposed to the direct
friction drive employed by the
American version, and were
offered with either a Simplex
built 285cc single cylinder 2
stroke engine, or a 348cc
Blackburne side valve single.*

NEW IMPERIAL

1925 New Imperial
350cc Motorcycle,
good condition.
Est. £1,600-1,800 *S*

NORMAN

1960 Norman 250cc Sports
Motorcycle, good original
condition.
£600-800 *S*

*Before 1939, only 98cc Villiers
engined autocycles were made by
the Ashford, Kent, firm of
Norman Cycles Ltd. They took
over the autocycle production
equipment from Rudge when that*
*company ceased production in
1939. In the late fifties their
machines were based on the
German built Achilles, but a
range of Villiers engined 2 stroke
lightweight machines were also
produced, ranging from 125cc to
250cc. The firm were later taken
over by Raleigh Industries in
Nottingham, and thereafter
concentrated on 50cc mopeds.*

Locate the Source

*The source of each
illustration in Miller's
can be found by checking
the code letters below
each caption with the
key to illustrations.*

NORTON, England, 1901-

- The company was founded by James Lansdowne Norton.
- The first motorcycles were fitted with Swiss Moto-Rêve engines, built in England under licence, and French Peugeot engines for the larger machines.
- Up until 1949, Norton single-cylinder motorcycles dominated Grand Prix racing.
- In 1953, Norton was bought by Associated Motor Cycles, manufacturers of AJS and Matchless, who already owned James and Frances Barnett.
- NVT (Norton-Villiers-Triumph Motorcycles Ltd) is now based at Shenstone, Staffordshire.

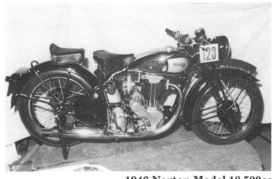

1946 Norton Model 18 500cc Motorcycle.
£3,000-3,500 *NOC*

1946 Norton Model 18 500cc Motorcycle.
£2,800-3,200 *VER*

1956 Norton Dominator 99 600cc Motorcycle.
£2,000-2,400 *VER*

1958 Norton Dominator Model 77 600cc Motorcycle, under restoration.
£1,000-1,500 *NOC*

1951 Norton Model 18 500cc Motorcycle, very good condition.
£3,500-4,000 *S*

Introduced in 1932, the Model 18 Norton continued in production as a big overhead valve single until 1954 and throughout that period retained the classic engine dimensions of 79 x 100mm. All examples also retained the original rigid frame unsprung at the rear, although telescopic forks were introduced in 1947.

1958 Norton International Motorcycle, excellent condition. **Est. £8,000-10,000** *S*

1958 was the last year of International production with the machines being built in very small numbers to special order. As a result Manx parts were often used in modified form.

1959 Norton Model 50 350cc Motorcycle, good condition. **£1,800-2,200** *S*

The smallest single in Norton's post-war range, the Model 50 featured a 71 x 88mm bore and stroke, overhead valve engine, driving through the AMC 4 speed gearbox, and by 1959 the featherbed frame.

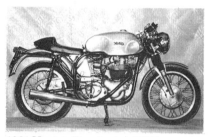

1961 Norton Dominator 99SS Café Racer. £1,500-1,700 *S*

The 99SS was announced in April of 1961 and had therefore one of the shortest production runs. The adoption of light alloy, taper tube pushrods and multi rate valve springs gave the 99SS some 44bhp at 6750rpm and a top speed in the order of 108mph.

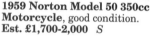

1959 Norton Model 50 350cc Motorcycle, good condition. **Est. £1,700-2,000** *S*

Introduced in 1933, and the smallest of Norton's famous singles, the Model 50 employed pushrod operated overhead valves and retained the original classic engine dimensions of 71 x 88mm for the next 30 years. The 50 MkII announced for the 1965 season was, however, a re-badged Matchless G-3. This example is a late 'real' Model 50 and features Norton's famous featherbed suspension and 4 speed posi-stop gearbox.

Locate the Source

The source of each illustration in Miller's can be found by checking the code letters below each caption with the key to illustrations.

1961 Norton Jubilee 250cc Motorcycle, good condition. **Est. £950-1,050** *S*

Designed by Bert Hopwood, the Jubilee featured a short stroke overhead valve twin engine in cycle parts that although conventional in appearance, made extensive use of steel pressings. Initially offered with full rear enclosure, a naked model was subsequently released.

1960 Norton Model 50 350cc Motorcycle, concours standard. **£3,400-3,800** *S*

1962 Norton Atlas 750cc Motorcycle, excellent condition. **Est. £2,500-2,700** *S*

Introduced in 1962 for export from the States in response to demands for yet more power, the 745cc Atlas featured a 73mm bore compared to the 650s 68mm, and a considerable improvement in torque whilst handling requirements were met by the featherbed frame.

1964 Norton Electra 400cc Motorcycle.
£1,500-2,000 *NOC*

The final development of the Jubilee/Navigator family, the Electra featured signal lights on the handlebars and an electric start.

1962 Norton Navigator 350cc Motorcycle.
£1,500-2,000 *NOC*

The Navigator was a larger version of the Norton Jubilee.

1965 Norton Atlas 750cc Motorcycle.
£2,500-3,000 *NOC*

Not in perfect condition.

1968 Norton Commando Fastback 750cc Motorcycle. Est. £2,500-3,000 *S*

The Commando was initially offered in 750cc form, although later models grew to 850cc. A notable innovation was the isolastic engine/gearbox mounting system to reduce the effects of engine vibrations.

**1969 Norton 750 'S'
Motorcycle.
£2,500-3,000** *S*

**1967 Norton Dominator 650
SS Motorcycle,** finished in
traditional silver with black and
chromium mudguards, good
condition.
Est. £2,500-3,000 *S*

*Norton's answer to the
Bonneville, the 650 SS featured
the proven Dominator twin
engine developed to produce
49bhp with maximum revs of
6800rpm.*

**1976 Norton Commando
850cc Motorcycle,** excellent
condition.
£3,500-4,000 *S*

**1988 Norton Classic 600cc
Motorcycle**, rotary engine.
£5,000-6,000 *NOC*

*Only 100 of this model were
made.*

1977 Norton Commando Mark III Motorcycle, with electric start.
£3,500-3,800 *PC*

1985 Norton Classic Rotary 588cc Motorcycle.
£5,600-5,900 *PC*

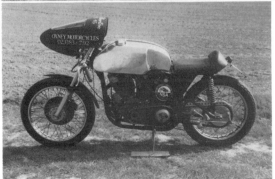

1991 Harmless Norton Vintage Sprinter 798cc Solo Motorcycle, 1943 Harley Davison WLA side valve Matchless G80 competition overhead valve, 1959 Norton wideline frame, V-twin, air cooled, overhead valve conversion, 4 stroke, 4 speed Norton gearbox, chain final drive, Norton roadholders telescopic front forks, Girling pivoted fork rear suspension, hand built special.
£3,000-3,500 *OxM*

O.E.C. BLACKBURNE

**1922 O.E.C. Blackburne
1000cc Motorcycle.
Est. £8,000-10,000** *S*

*One of the smaller companies,
O.E.C. (Osborn Engineering
Company) produced high quality
machines which often
incorporated unusual design
features. This example from the
early 1920s is typical of the large
capacity V-twins, which were
marketed by many firms who
had an eye on the lucrative
sidecar market.*

OVERSEAS

**1914 Overseas 490cc
Motorcycle**, fully restored and
eligible for the Pioneer Run.
£5,000-7,000 *S*

*Built by the Overseas Motor
Company of 1A, Johnstone
Street, Ladywood, Birmingham,
the Overseas motorcycle was built
in single cylinder and V-twin
form from 1909 until 1916,
mainly for the British Colonial
market.*

**1961 Panther 120 650cc
Motorcycle.
£1,500-1,700** *S*

*Panther's final development of
their illustrious big single to be
put into production, was in
response to the growing need for
a competitor to the large capacity
twins that were making inroads
into Panther's traditional sidecar
market.*

PANTHER

**1936 Panther 250cc
Motorcycle.
£1,300-1,500** *S*

*Cleckheaton, Yorkshire, was the
home of the P & M Panther made
by Phelon and Moore, and the
firm were in busines there from
1900 until 1965, eking out the
last ten years of their existence in
Receivership, but still producing
machines. The firm pioneered
sloping engines, selling the
licence for this configuration to
Humber Coventry as well, and
were still producing this type to
the last.*

**1948 Panther 100 600cc
Motorcycle. £900-1,100** *S*

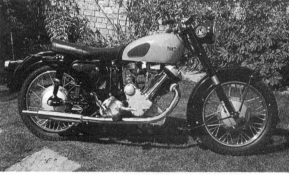

**1952 Panther M100 600cc
Motorcycle,** good condition.
Est. £1,500-1,800 *S*

*Panther's Model 100 had been
perfected during the pre-war
years to the extent that it was to
remain largely unaltered post-
war, except for the adoption of
telescopic forks and a sprung
rear frame, whilst continuing to
offer characteristics and
performance that few other
machines could match.*

PARILLA OLYMPIA

Parilla Olympia 115cc 160 Motorcycle, 53 x 52mm bore and stroke, compression ratio 7.1:1, 4 speed gearbox, horizontal mounted cylinder, Del'orto carburettor mounted above the engine, telescopic front forks and twin shock absorber, swing arm rear suspension, drum brakes by Gremeca, alloy rims and wire spokes, electrics by C.E.V.
Est. £1,800-2,200 *P*

Miller's is a price
GUIDE not a price
LIST

PUCH

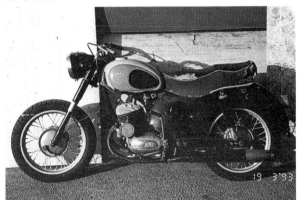

**c1965 Puch 250cc Motorcycle.
£100-150** *S*

This machine is believed to be a 250cc 'split single' of the type produced by the company during the 1960s.

QUADRANT

**c1919 Quadrant Motorcycle Combination.
Est. £5,500-7,000** *S*

Motorcycle production at Quadrant Works, Sheepcote Street, Birmingham began as early as 1901 initially using the ubiquitous Minerva engine but from 1903 the W.L. Lloyd designed machines used engines of their own manufacture.

RALEIGH

1924 Raleigh Model 6 348cc Motorcycle, 2¾hp.
£1,500-2,000 *RSS*

Built by the famous Nottingham cycle manufacturer this overhead valve model represents one of the company's more sporting models.

1925 Raleigh 350cc Sport Motorcycle, good condition.
£4,000-4,500 *S*

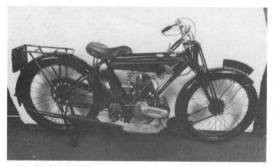

1924 Raleigh Motorcycle, 2¾hp, side valve, 4 stroke, 3 speed hand change.
£2,500-3,000 *ROB*

1929 Raleigh Model 15 De Luxe 248cc Motorcycle.
£1,500-2,000 *RSS*

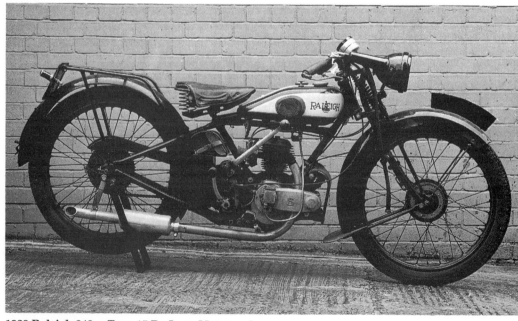

1929 Raleigh 248cc Type 15 De Luxe Motorcycle,
Sturmey Archer engine and gearbox, electric lighting, dynamo fitted, John Bull knee grip rubbers, Cowley speedometer.
£1,200-1,500 *P*

1928 Raleigh 250cc Sports Motorcycle, single cylinder, side valve engined model, Sturmey-Archer 3 speed hand change gearbox, painted black with red and gold coachlining.
£2,000-2,400 *S*

Best known these days for their pushbikes, Raleigh's Nottingham factory had 3 separate periods of motorcycle production from 1899 to 1906, from 1919 to the early thirties and then again concentrating on mopeds after WWII.

RELIANT

1956 Reliant Regal Mark III 747cc Coupé, side valve engine, glass fibre body, totally rebuilt.
£2,800-3,200 *RSS*

The world's first mass-produced fibreglass car.

REX ACME

1904 Rexette 5hp Forecar Motorcycle.
Est. £11,000-12,000 *S*

The Rex Motor Manufacturing Co Ltd of Coventry produced the Rexette with a car-type frame and water-cooled 5hp single cylinder engine started by a handle and a 2 speed gearbox with brakes on all 3 wheels at a price of 100 guineas. As early as 1904 the Tricar was used for commercial purposes such as postal and trade deliveries and it was gradually moving further and further away from its motorcycle origins towards the characteristics of the early motorcar with larger engines and with no pedal assistance. Handlebar steering was replaced with the steering wheel, weather proofing was added and more comfortable seating.

1928 Rex Acme TT8 Sports Replica 350cc Motorcycle.
£5,500-6,500 *NWB*

RICKMAN

1969 Rickman Metisse Triumph T120R 650cc Motorcycle, excellent condition.
Est. £2,600-3,000 *S*

From 1959, the Rickman brothers specialised in producing frame kits, mainly from the Honda 900cc, Suzuki GS 1000 and Kawasaki ZI, Z900 and Z1000 engines, these were successfully exported to many countries including the USA.

1973 Rickman Triumph Metisse 650cc Motorcycle.
£2,800-3,200 *SS*

ROYAL ENFIELD, England, 1898-1971

- Formerly a branch of the pioneer make, Eadie (England 1898-1903), Royal Enfield built three- wheelers with De Dion engines and then motorcycles mounted with Minerva/MAG/De Dion engines.
- Royal Enfield's post-WWI production models were mainly fitted with their own engine units.

- In the 1930s, the factory produced successful trials machines.
- During WWII, Royal Enfield supplied the Forces with 346cc single valve and overhead valve models.
- The Interceptor (with a Rickman frame) and the Continental were the last models produced by the company.

1921 Royal Enfield 2¼hp Motorcycle, good condition. **£1,500-1,800** *S*

Royal Enfield's 2¼hp lightweight is representative of the good quality machines of the class that emerged in WWI in response to the demand for economical and robust transport.

1914 Royal Enfield Model 180 6hp 770cc Motorcycle Combination, excellent condition, Pioneer eligible. **Est. £7,500-8,500** *S*

Introduced for the 1912 season, Royal Enfield's new 6hp model was designed specifically for sidecar use and featured a 771cc (76cm x 85cm) JAP side valve V-twin 2 speed gearbox and chain final drive, whilst the sidecar was of Royal Enfield manufacture with, by 1914, 2 styles of wicker and one of coachwork being offered.

1921 Royal Enfield 2¼hp 225cc Model 200 Motorcycle, traditional livery, good condition. **£1,500-2,000** *S*

1931 Royal Enfield Model K 976cc Motorcycle. **£2,000-3,000** *S*

A good example of a large capacity side valve V-twin designed for sidecar work.

1960 Triumph Motorcycle,
4 plug cylinder head, high
compression pistons, high lift
cams and lightened valves,
gear and flywheels,
megaphone silencer, racing
seat, rear sets and grab rail,
blue and silver paintwork, 12
volt electronics.
Est. £2,200-2,800   *S*

**1951 Triumph Speed Twin
Motorcycle,** one owner from
new, all documentation,
concours condition.
£5,500-6,500   *DG*

**1938 Triumph Speed
Twin 500cc Motorcycle,**
maroon livery, good all
round condition.
Est. £3,000-3,500   *S*

**1960 Triumph 3TU 350cc
Motorcycle,** single cam, 3 speed,
head and rockers cast integral,
barrel and top half crankcase are
also one.
£24,000-26,000   *CM*

*This motorcycle is the only one of its
kind built.*
*The engine does run, although this
bike has never been used on the
road.*

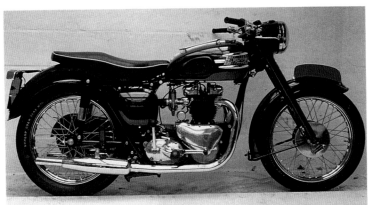

**1959 Triumph
Thunderbird 650cc
Motorcycle.**
£4,500-5,000 *VER*

**1964 Triumph T90
Tiger 350cc Solo
Motorcycle,** V-twin, air-
cooled, overhead valve, 4
stroke, 4 speed gearbox,
chain final drive,
Triumph telescopic front
forks, Girling pivoted
fork rear suspension.
£1,800-2,000 *OxM*

**1964 Triumph
Bonneville 650cc
Motorcycle.**
£3,500-4,500 *VER*

**c1965 Triumph 350cc
Motorcycle Prototype,**
overhead camshaft, 180°
crank with gear driven
cam, cable operated disc
brakes.
£30,000+ *CM*

*This was the last
Triumph twin that
Edward Turner
designed.*

1968 Triumph T120 Bonneville Solo Motorcycle, vertical twin, air-cooled overhead valve, 4 stroke, 4 speed Triumph gearbox, chain final drive, Triumph telescopic front forks, Girling pivoted fork rear suspension.
£1,800-2,200 *OxM*

1970 Triumph Trophy Motorcycle.
£1,800-2,200 *VER*

1971 Triumph Trail Blazer SS 250cc Motorcycle, good condition.
£450-550 *S*

1972 Triumph TR7V Tiger 750cc Solo Motorcycle, vertical twin, air-cooled, overhead valve, 4 stroke, 5 speed Triumph gearbox, chain final drive, Triumph telescopic front forks, Hagon pivoted fork rear suspension.
£2,500-3,000 *OxM*

1973 Triumph Hurricane 750cc Motorcycle.
£4,000-5,000 *VER*

1972 Triumph Bonneville T120 650cc Motorcycle.
Est. £2,300-2,600 *S*

1973 Triumph TR5T 500cc Motorcycle, twin engine unit, alloy petrol tank, chromium plated sports mudguards, red and black livery.
Est. £2,500-2,800 *S*

1974 Triumph T150V Trident 750cc Solo Motorcycle, vertical triple, air-cooled, overhead valve, 4 stroke, 5 speed gearbox, chain final drive, Triumph telescopic front forks, Girling pivoted fork rear suspension.
£3,500-4,000 *OxM*

Mid-1970s Triumph Cardinal 3 cylinder Motorcycle.
£8,000-9,000 *CM*

This model was ordered by the Saudi Arabian Police, but was never delivered, It has never had petrol in its tank, and has only been run at the factory.

1976 Triumph T160V Trident 750cc Solo Motorcycle, inclined vertical triple, air-cooled, overhead valve, 4 stroke engine, 5 speed Triumph gearbox, chain final drive, Triumph telescopic front forks, Girling pivoted fork rear suspension.
£3,000-3,500 *OxM*

1979 Triumph T140V Bonneville Solo Motorcycle, vertical twin, air-cooled, overhead valve, 4 stroke engine, 5 speed Triumph gearbox, chain final drive, Triumph telescopic front forks, Girling pivoted fork rear suspension.
£2,500-2,800 *OxM*

1980 Triumph T140 750cc Bonneville Motorcycle, with 'Thruxton conversion', customised to Café Racer.
£3,000-3,500 *PC*

1982 Triumph TR65 650cc
Thunderbird Motorcycle.
£3,700-3,900 *PC*

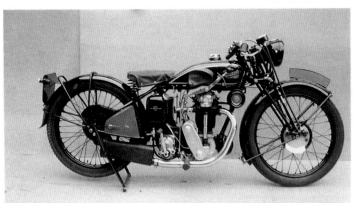

1930 Velocette Model KNSS
Motorcycle, overhead
camshaft.
£4,400-4,600 *VER*

1981 Triumph T140
Bonneville 744cc Motorcycle.
£2,700-3,000 *S*

1934 Velocette KTS 350cc
Motorcycle, overhead camshaft.
£4,500-5,500 *VER*

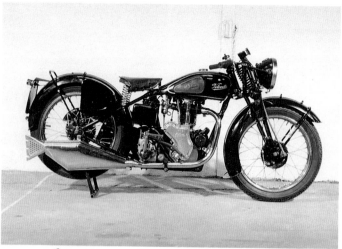

1938 Velocette Mac 350cc Motorcycle, black and gold livery, original example.
£1,800-2,000 *S*

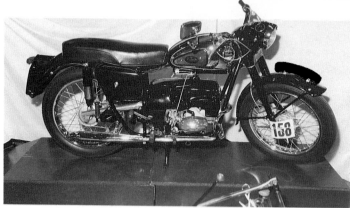

1952 Velocette Valiant, 192cc Motorcycle, sporting overhead valve model.
£1,000-2,500 *LVC*

1950 Mark VIII Velocette 350cc Motorcycle, overhead camshaft.
£19,000-21,000 *VER*

1955 Velocette LE 200cc Motorcycle, flat, water-cooled, side valve twin cylinder engine, shaft drive, semi-enclosed.
£220-250 *S*

**1952 Vincent Black Shadow
1000cc Motorcycle.**
£10,000-12,000 *VER*

**1964 Velocette Vogue
192cc Motorcycle.**
£800-2,000 *LVC*
*This is the last variation on
the 'LE' fibreglass body spine
frame.*

**1958 Velocette LE 200cc
Motorcycle,** horizontally
opposed water-cooled engine,
in-unit gearbox, spring
frames, shaft final drive, leg
guards, hand change gearbox,
scooter-like side panels,
lacking seat, requires
restoration.
Est. £400-600 *S*

**1956 Vincent Series D Open Rapide
Motorcycle,** concours condition.
£11,000-13,000 *DG*

1969 Aermacchi/Harley-Davidson ACA d'Oro 350cc Racing Motorcycle.
Est. £5,000-6,500 *S*

The engine detail of
1969 Aermacchi/Harley-Davidson ACA d'Oro 350cc Racing Motorcycle.

1983 Suzuki RG 500 XR45 500cc Racing Motorcycle, Square Four 2 stroke engine.
Est. £7,000-8,000 *S*

1953 Royal Enfield 1 Bullet Scrambler, reinforced handlebar clamps, tucked-in exhaust, roller bearing big end, high compression piston, gas flowed head, race ready condition.
Est. £1,800-2,200 *S*

c1962 Triumph 5TA Trials 500cc Motorcycle, Norton front forks, Koni rear shock absorbers, alloy mudguards and fuel tank, high level exhaust system, 21in front wheel, good condition.
£600-800 *S*

1943 BSA M20 500cc motorcycle.
£1,200-1,400 *MVT*
Totally rebuilt to present condition.

1943 Harley-Davidson WLC 750cc Motorcycle, V-twin, side valve.
£3,000-6,000 *MVT*

This model is ex-Canadian Army. It is similar to the American Army WLA but has interchangeable wheels and different lighting.

Parts availability fairly good, but expensive, compared with British WD motorcycle parts.

1967 BSA WD B40 350cc Motorcycle.
£900-1,300 *BOC*

This is a genuine ex-Army motorcycle. These are rare as most were broken up for parts once they had ceased to be used.

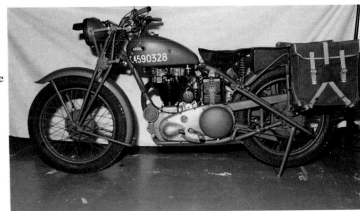

1942 Ariel W/NG 350cc Motorcycle.
£1,600-1,800 *MVT*

1941 Matchless G3 350cc Motorcycle.
£1,600-1,900 *AMOC*

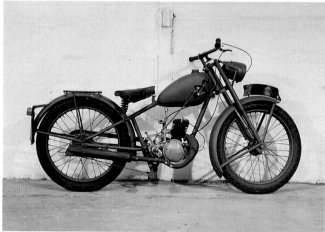

1940 Royal Enfield 'Flying Flea' Model RE Motorcycle, later front forks, in military trim.
£400-600 *S*
This motorcycle was displayed in a museum until recently. It would appear to be fitted with later front forks. A good example of this interesting model.

1944 Royal Enfield WD/RE 125cc Motorcycle, single cylinder, 2 stroke.
£700-1,000 *MVT*

Popular bikes with aeronautica memorabilia collectors as they were used at Arnhem, Holland in 1944 (A Bridge Too Far). The civilian version of these bikes is known to have been modified to cash in on the vastly more sought after military version, which also command higher prices and sell far more easily. Parts availability is poor.

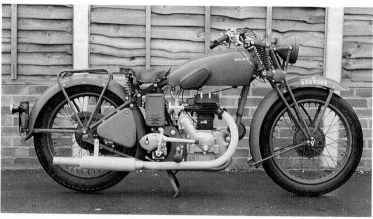

1940 Royal Enfield WD/C 350cc Motorcycle, single cylinder, side valve.
£12,000-14,000 *MVT*

This motorcycle is quite different from Royal Enfield's overhead valve version, the WD/CO. The main differences are the centre stand, the gearbox, the rear wheel and the frame. Later WD/Cs had luggage racks, oil filters on the timing cover and steel (not alloy) brakeplates. Parts availability is fair.

1962 RAP Imperial 49cc Moped, Earles type front forks, 'swinging' fork rear suspension with full mudguards, the refurbished, although dismantled engine is also present.
£125-150 *S*

1950 Cymota 45cc Pedal Cycle, with bolt-on engine.
£100-450 *NAC*

1957 Lambretta Model D 150cc Scooter.
£3,300-3,600 *VMSC*

1959 Automoto 49cc Autocycle, red and white, original condition.
Est. £150-200 *S*

Four Grand Prix one-ninth Scale Motorcycle Models, by Protar, Italian, comprising Moto Morini, Gilera, Moto Benelli and Moto Guzzi, with original boxes.
£100-150 *S*

Two pairs of E. B. Meyrovitz 'Luxor' Motor Racing Goggles, nickel plated brass with perforated gauze vented frames and laminated glass lenses, No 4, c1920, and No 7, 1930.
£280-350 each *BKS*

l. **A Herbert Johnson motor racing helmet and US pattern Polaroid goggles,** c1956.
£200-250
r. **A pair of Les Leston racing goggles, and a Kangol Skidmaster racing helmet,** silk lined, with adjustable harness fitting, c1958.
£350-400 *BKS*

A selection of 20 Motorcycle Sport Magazines, complete run from Vols. IV to XXIV of 1963 to 1983, publishers bindings.
Est. £360-440 *S*

A Simpson full-face racing helmet, black painted and decorated with Road-Runner logo, as worn by Paul Newman in late 1970s.
Est. £450-700 *BKS*

Four advertising posters comprising BSA 500 Twin, BSA V-Twin, 'Know Your BSA', framed and glazed, 30 x 20½in (76 x 52cm), and another, BSA Motocross, 16 x 21in (41 x 53cm).
£12-20 *S*

Three advertising posters, comprising Ariel Square Four, BSA 500 Twin and Triumph Motors, and a letter from BSA Sales Manager with sales brochure.
£18-25 *S*

Three advertising posters, comprising Triumph Motorräder, Ariel Square Four and NSU.
£12-20 *S*

An Electric Speedway Racing Board Game, by BGL, London, with 8 riders, together with another Speedway game. **£60-100** *S*

A Mini-Motor Authorised Dealer tinplate advertising sign, double sided. **Est. £60-90** *S*

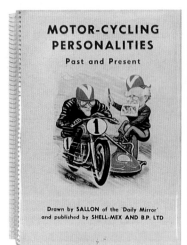

Motor-Cycling Personalities, Past and Present, drawn by Sallon of the Daily Mirror, published by Shell-Mex and BP Ltd. **£25-50** *S*

An Acme Advertising Sign for Triumph, light and dark blue perspex, c1950s. **£240-260** *S*

An Acme Illuminated Advertising Sign for BSA, the metal light box with perspex front, wired for illumination, c1950s, 23½in (60cm) wide. **£200-260** *S*

c1933 Royal Enfield Single Cylinder 500cc Twin Port Model L.F. Motorcycle, some parts missing.
Est. £1,000-1,800 *P*

1948 Royal Enfield 499cc Motorcycle.
£1,600-2,000 *S*

1922 Royal Enfield 2¼hp Motorcycle, 2 stroke single cylinder 225cc engine, 2 speed hand change gearbox with chain final drive.
£1,000-1,200 *S*

The post WWI years saw an increased demand for personal transport and a growing number of lightweights appeared, including the Royal Enfield 2¼hp model. The quality of these lightweights varied enormously and the Enfield models represented the better end of the market.

1960 Royal Enfield Meteor Minor Sports 500cc Motorcycle.
£4,000-5,000 *S*

The Sports variant of the Meteor Minor featured special cams and springs to increase the engine output to 33bhp at 6500rpm as opposed to the touring models 30bhp at 6250rpm whilst chrome plated mudguards and dropped handlebars were fitted to reflect its sporting nature.

Locate the Source

The source of each illustration in Miller's can be found by checking the code letters below each caption with the key to illustrations.

1960 Royal Enfield 150cc Prince Motorcycle, good condition.
Est. £600-800 *S*

Developed from the Ensign models, the Prince, introduced in 1959, featured full circle flywheels and a pivoted fork frame, whilst a fully enclosed chain case helped to prolong chain life.

RUDGE

**c1925 Rudge Four 500cc
Motorcycle.
Est. £3,000-3,200** *S*

**1928 Rudge Special 500cc
Motorcycle,** fair condition.
£3,000-3,500 *S*

*The 1928 Special represented a
more up-market version of the
standard machine and featured in
addition to the newly introduced
gearbox and 8 inch brakes, an
adjustable damper for the front
forks.*

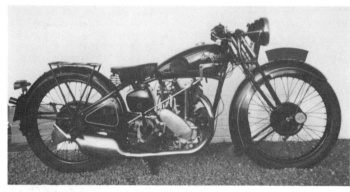

1930 Rudge 350cc Motorcycle,
single cylinder, 4 valve radial
head, original condition,
unrestored.
£3,000-4,000 *PC*

*One of the first road-going 350
radial Rudges.*

**1936 Rudge Special
Motorcycle Combination.
£3,000-3,500** *HOLL*

**1933 Rudge Ulster GP 500cc
Racing Motorcycle,** with a BTH
magneto, TT9 carburettor, good
condition throughout.
£2,500-3,000 *S*

1937 Rudge Rapid 250cc Motorcycle. Est. £2,000-2,500 *S*

1938 Rudge Special 500cc Motorcycle.
£3,400-3,600 *S*

*The new 4 valve arrangement
introduced by Rudge for the 1930
season brought them success in the
1930 TT and established the
pattern of their production
machines of the 1930s. The
Special was a touring bike derived
directly from the Ulster and
featured enclosed rocker gear,
more favoured by the less sporting
enthusiast.*

**1938 Rudge Rapid 250cc
Motorcycle,** fully restored.
Est. £3,000-3,800 *S*

*Introduced in 1936, the Rapid
featured a 2 valve version of the
famous overhead valve engine and
most of the other features expected
of Rudge machines.*

SCOTT, England, 1909-1981

- The Scott motorcycle took its name from its pre-WWI designer, A. A. Scott.
- The Scott motorcycle was unique among veteran and vintage machines in being a twin cylinder, liquid cooled, 2 stroke.
- Scott enjoyed great success in competition racing. This resulted in both factory replicas and privately modified machines appearing.
- The Scott engine was further developed in the post war years and formed the basis of the Silk motorcycle which was manufactured during the 1970s.

1930 Scott 2 Speed 2 Stroke Motorcycle.
£3,800-4,000 *S*

**1930 Scott TT Replica 596cc
Motorcycle,** good condition.
Est. £3,000-4,000 *S*

**1929 Scott TT Replica 500cc
Motorcycle.**
£5,300-5,700 *VER*

SEELEY

c1975 Seeley Weslake 750 Motorcycle, 741cc overhead valve V-twin engine, 73 x 88.5mm bore and stroke, pre-unit 4 speed gearbox, telescopic front forks, twin shock absorbers, swing arm rear end, wire wheels, disc brakes back and front with alloy rims.
Est. £3,600-4,400 *P*

SINGER

1912 Singer 500cc Motorcycle.
£6,300-6,700 *VER*

SUNBEAM

1922 Sunbeam 500cc Motorcycle Combination.
£10,000-11,000 *VER*

SUN

1953 Sun 98cc Motorcycle.
Est. £600-800 *S*

The Sun Cycle & Fittings Company were another Birmingham motorcycle factory who were early on the scene in 1906 and who continued production (albeit sporadically after the end of the 1920s) until 1961, latterly under the aegis of Raleigh Industries in Nottingham.

1925 Sunbeam Model 9 500cc Motorcycle, good original condition.
£5,500-6,000 *S*

1923/24 Sunbeam Model 1 Roadster 347cc Motorcycle, in fully restored working condition.
£3,500-4,000 *RJ*

**c1928 Sunbeam Model 8 350cc
Motorcycle,** contemporary bulb
horn, mechanically sound,
finished in traditional black and
gold livery.
£4,200-4,600 *S*

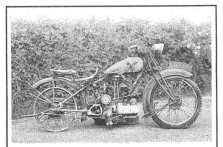

**1934 Sunbeam Model 9 493cc
Motorcycle,** unrestored
condition.
£900-1,100 *S*

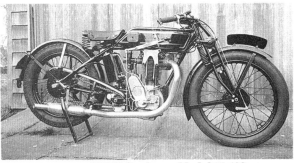

**1927/8 Sunbeam Model 90 493cc
Motorcycle,** excellent condition.
£12,000-14,000 *S*

*Sunbeam's Model 90 493cc and
the 346cc Model 80 were TT
replicas in the truest sense, closely
following the specifications of the
works machines that had proved
so successful in road racing
throughout the 1920s. Featuring
hairspring valves, 3 speed
gearboxes and the tall 80 x 98mm
overhead valve engine in a rigid
frame with good brakes, the 90 was
the epitomy of a 1920s racing motorcycle.*

**1950 Sunbeam S7 500cc
Motorcycle,** good condition.
Est. £1,600-1,700 *S*

*Designed by Erling Poppe, the
overhead cam, twin cylinder
Sunbeam S7 provided for those
seeking a gentlemanly tourer.
Featuring telescopic forks, plunger
rear spring saddle, comfort was at
a premium whilst the engine
offered enough performance to
enable good averages to be
maintained on the roads of the
day.*

Miller's is a price
GUIDE not a price
LIST

**1939 Sunbeam Lion 598cc
Motorcycle.**
£700-1,000 *S*

*The Sunbeam factory in
Wolverhampton passed through a
number of hands during the
1930s, John Marston Ltd
relinquishing control to ICI for a
period following which Associated
Motorcycles took over for a while
before selling the company to BSA
during WWII.*

1947 Sunbeam S7 500cc Motorcycle, good condition.
£1,700-2,000 *S*

1950 Sunbeam S7 500cc Motorcycle, good condition.
£2,000-2,200 *S*

Erling Poppe's Sunbeam S7 was designed as a luxury tourer at a time of some post-war austerity. Its distinctive appearance, chunky 16 inch tyres and underslung worm drive set the bike in a class of its own and the bike also featured a spring frame, enclosed electrical gear and instantly detachable interchangeable wheels. All this luxury sold for £175 plus £47-5s-0d purchase tax.

1956 Sunbeam S8 500cc Motorcycle.
£1,200-1,400 *S*

SUZUKI

1976 Suzuki GT500 Motorcycle, good condition.
Est. £1,800-2,000 *S*

Originally introduced in 1967 as the T500 Cobra, or Titan to our American cousins, Suzuki's largest 2 stroke twin offered exciting performance and good handling, combined with a mechanical robustness seldom found in a machine of its performance. These factors united to keep the model in production until 1977 with only minor updates.

1950 Sunbeam S8 500cc Motorcycle.
£1,700-1,900 *S*

TRITON

c1960 Triton 650cc Special Motorcycle. £2,300-3,000 *S*

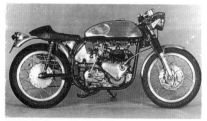

1991 Triton 650CC Motorcycle.
£2,000-2,500 *S*

The definitive Café Racer, the Triton is the result of the marriage of a Triumph engine, ideally a pre-unit Bonneville or Tiger 110, and a Norton featherbed frame.

1950/60s Triton 650cc Motorcycle, good standard cosmetically and finished in traditional Norton colours of black and silver with fine red lining.
£2,200-2,600 *S*

TRIUMPH (TEC) England, 1903-

- The Coventry company was founded by Siegfried Bettmann and Maurice Schulte in 1897 and started by producing bicycles. In 1902 a 220cc machine with a Minerva engine was produced.
- Schulte designed Triumph's first single cylinder single valve engine (3.5hp).
- Up until 1929, Triumph, England and Triumph, Germany worked closely together. Following their estrangement, Triumph, England became known as TEC, Triumph Engineering Company Limited.
- In 1936, Ariel bought out Triumph and their leading designer, Edward Turner was put in charge.
- Triumph were responsible for supplying thousands of machines to the Forces during WWI and WWII.
- Famous Triumph riders include Lyons, Halford, Jefferies and the McCandless brothers, amongst others.

1909 Triumph 3½hp 470cc Motorcycle.
Est. £4,000-5,000 *S*

1917 Triumph Model H 550cc Motorcycle, side valve.
£3,400-3,600 *VER*

This motorcycle was widely used by all protagonists during WWI as a despatch rider's machine.

1913 Triumph 499cc Motorcycle,
3 speed hub gear and clutch, fitted with a replica wicker sidecar, a full complement of period lights and a horn.
£5,000-6,000 *S*

One of the most significant advances in motorcycle design was the gradual introduction of variable gearing in all its forms, enabling motorcycles and their riders to conquer inclines that formerly would have defeated their single speed forebears. Another beneficiary was the sidecar, which became a practical form of transport.

Miller's is a price **GUIDE** not a price **LIST**

1910 Triumph 499cc Motorcycle.
£3,200-3,700 *S*

c1918 Triumph 225cc Motorcycle,
2 stroke, originally known as the junior lightweight. Est. £700-1,200 *P*

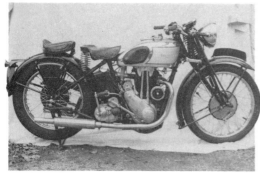

1936 Triumph Tiger 90 500cc
Motorcycle, overhead valve.
£5,800-6,200 *PC*

Introduced in May 1936 following the collapse of Triumph Motorcycles in 1935, this particular machine was registered 5 days after the announcement of the new range of Tiger 70, 80, and 90. By September it had been revamped completely with a new frame, gearbox and cycle parts. This is a very rare version and is noteable for its twin exhaust pipes, 8 inch diameter brakes which are interlinked and a footbrake which has a locking device to enable it to be a parking brake.

1925 Triumph 500cc Sports Motorcycle, fitted with girder forks, hand change gearbox, rigid rear frame, painted in traditional Triumph grey and green with black frame, in running order.
£1,600-2,000 *S*

1938 Triumph Model 5T Speed
Twin Motorcycle.
£4,000-5,000 *VMCC*

First introduced by Triumph in June 1937.

1946 Triumph Tiger 100 500cc
Motorcycle, restored.
Est. £3,800-4,200 *S*

1947 Triumph Tiger 100 500cc
Motorcycle, good condition.
£3,800-4,200 *S*

1950 Triumph Thunderbird
Sprung Hub 650cc Solo
Motorcycle, restored.
£1,300-1,500 *S*

Edward Turner launched the new Thunderbird at Montlhery in September 1949 with two of the new machines covering 500 miles at an average speed including stops in excess of 90mph, then proceeding to lap the circuit at over 100mph before being ridden back to Meriden.

**1954 Triumph Terrier T15
150cc Motorcycle.
£350-450** *S*

**1948 Triumph Speed Twin
500cc Motorcycle,** restored.
£4,200-4,600 *S*

*Renowned for its simplicity and
lightness the Speed Twin engine
was to be the backbone of
Triumph's post-war production
and its versatility was proved by
its excellent record on and off the
road and on the track.*

**1958 Triumph 3TA 490cc
Motorcycle,** good condition.
£2,000-2,500 *S*

**1953 Triumph Model TRW
500cc Display Team
Motorcycle.
£1,000-1,500** *S*

*Triumph's post-war TRW twin
was a sturdy machine aimed at
the lucrative Ministry of Defence
market and developed using
experience gained from the
wartime service of Triumph
machines. Telescopic front forks
were a new feature although rigid
rear suspension remained
standard on the TRW. The 1953
models as tested by 'Motor
Cycling' had coil ignition, weighed
only 320lbs, developed some
17bhp and had a top speed of
almost 74mph.*

**1959 Triumph 6T
'Thunderbird' 650cc
Motorcycle.
Est. £2,200-2,500** *S*

**1958 Triumph T20 Tiger Cub
Motorcycle.
£800-1,000** *S*

**1959 Triumph Tiger Cub T20C
Trials 200cc Motorcycle,** in
need of restoration.
Est. £600-900 *S*

*Introduced in 1957, the T20C
competition version of the Tiger
Cub featured an upswept exhaust,
trials tyres and crankcase shield,
and the newly introduced pivoted
fork frame common to the road
variants.*

1960 Triumph 3TA Twenty-One 350cc Motorcycle, good condition.
£1,400-1,700 *S*

1961 Triumph 650cc Motorcycle.
£3,700-4,200 *S*

Edward Turner's pre-war Speed Twin was a landmark machine in the history of the British motorcycle and set the fashion for Triumph's post-war production. The overhead valve machines were well engineered and responded well to post-factory tuning. The Tiger 110 with its 650cc engine continued in the best Triumph traditions, developing some 42bhp and the T120 introduced in 1958 was more powerful with 46bhp 'on tap'.
The T120 was to be called the Bonneville, reflecting the achievements of the bike on the Bonneville Salt Flats.

1963 Triumph Tiger 90 350cc Motorcycle.
£1,600-1,800 *S*

1964 Triumph 3TA Type 21 350cc Motorcycle, good original condition.
£1,000-1,200 *S*

Edward Turner chose the first of the new unit construction C series twin engines to unveil Triumph's new enclosed styling theme with the Type 21's introduction. Apart from the 'bathtub' enclosure and valanced-front mudguard the new 350cc twin followed Triumph design closely.

1961 Triumph Thunderbird 6T Motorcycle, good condition.
£1,600-2,000 *S*

1963 Triumph Tiger Cub 200cc Motorcycle.
£700-1,000 *S*

1965 Triumph 120 Thunderbird 650cc Motorcycle.
£2,500-3,000 *S*

Triumph's 650cc Thunderbird was just one of a long line of famous vertical twin cylinder models which followed Edward Turner's first Speed Twin, and which included the Tiger 100's and Bonnevilles.

1968 Triumph T120 Bonneville 650cc Motorcycle.
£2,500-3,000 *PC*

1970 Triumph T100 Tiger Daytona 500cc Motorcycle, twin carburettors.
£2,700-3,100 *PC*

1970 Triumph T120 Bonneville 650cc Motorcycle, totally original condition.
£2,700-3,100 *PC*

1975 Triumph 750cc Trident Motorcycle.
£1,900-2,300 *S*

Introduced in the early 1970s, Triumph's transverse mounted 3 cylinder overhead valve Trident was the first entirely new model for many years.

c1970 Triumph Trident T150 750cc Motorcycle.
Est. £2,650-3,000 *S*

1972 Triumph T150 Trident 750cc Motorcycle, made to US specifications.
£3,700-4,100 *PC*

1972 Triumph TR6R Trophy 650cc Motorcycle.
£3,400-3,800 *PC*

**1977 Triumph Silver Jubilee
Bonneville 750cc Motorcycle,**
good condition.
Est. £2,500-3,000 *S*

*Produced by the Meriden Co-
Operative to commemorate Queen
Elizabeth II's 25 years as
monarch, the Silver Jubilee
Bonneville featured a special
silver finish with red, white and
blue lining and chrome plated
timing and drive covers.
Production was limited to 2,400
examples for all markets.*

**1977 Triumph Silver Jubilee
Bonneville 744cc Motorcycle.**
Est. £2,000-3,000 *S*

**1981 Triumph Bonneville
750cc Motorcycle.**
£3,000-3,500 *S*

*Designed to capitalise on the
T140's ability as a long distance
tourer, the Executive variant
offered by Meriden in the early 80s
was equipped with a full
complement of hand luggage and
a handlebar mounted fairing,
whilst a smoked black and red
finish further distinguished the
model.*

**1980 Triumph T140 Bonneville
750cc Motorcycle,** good
condition.
£2,000-2,300 *S*

**1979 Triumph TR7RV 750cc
Motorcycle,** twin cyclinder,
overhead valve, single
carburettor, Amal concentric, 5
speed gearbox, built at Meriden.
£1,350-1,750 *P*

**1981 Triumph TR65
Thunderbird 650cc
Motorcycle.**
£3,600-4,000 *PC*

*This model was the last run of
motorcycles before the factory at
Meriden closed.*

**Triumph T140V Bonneville
750cc Motorcycle,** US
specifications, reasonable
condition.
Est. £1,400-1,600 *P*

VELOCETTE, England, 1904-68

- Founded by Percy and Eugene Goodman, Velocette succeeded Ormonde, VMC and Veloce.
- Percy Goodman designed the first overhead camshaft model in 1925 and this formed the basis of all subsequent Velocettes, including the KTT Mk VIII racing model.
- Velocette was famous for their racing machines and won, amongst others, the Isle of Man TT, and were renowned for their speed and reliability on the Continent.
- Famous Velocette riders include Stanley Woods, Alec Bennett, Les Archer and Freddy Hicks.

1913 Veloce 293cc Motorcycle, inlet over exhaust, good condition.
£6,000-7,000 S

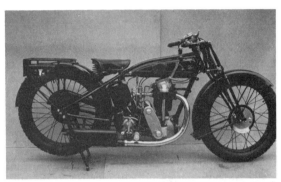

c1920 Velocette 275cc Motorcycle.
Est. £1,500-3,000 S

1926 Velocette Model K 350cc Motorcycle, overhead camshaft.
£7,700-8,300 VER

This was the first overhead camshaft model made by Velocette.

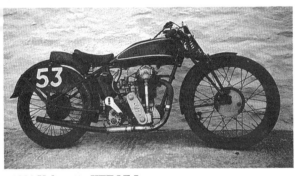

c1930 Velocette KTT MkI Motorcycle, original condition.
£8,000-9,000 S

Velocette's first production racing model, the KTT, was based on their 1928 Junior TT winner and helped the firm to capitalise on their success and ensure a healthy entry in club races of their machines. With a light strong frame the handling was secure whilst large drum brakes ensured good retardation. The overhead camshaft engine's breathing was assisted by a tuned open pipe and a 3 speed gearbox looked after the transmission.

Miller's is a price GUIDE not a price LIST

1932 Velocette GTP 250cc Motorcycle, restoration project.
£300-400 S

The GTP is a typical lightweight machine of its period with girder fork front suspension and rigid rear frame.

1933 Velocette KTS 350cc Motorcycle.
£4,500-5,000 S

Introduced in 1932 as a replacement for the KTP twinport 350cc, the KTS was essentially a KSS fitted with touring mudguards and tyres.

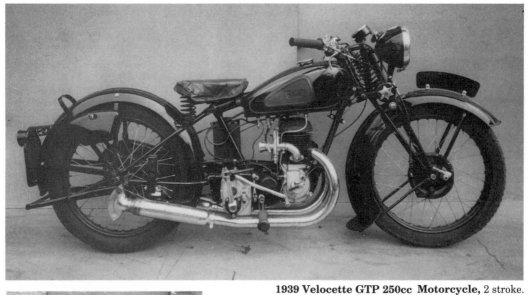

1939 Velocette GTP 250cc Motorcycle, 2 stroke.
£1,600-2,000 *VER*

**1934 Velocette MOV 250cc
Motorcycle.
£2,000-2,500** *S*

*Originally conceived to fill the
perceived gap between the GTP 2
stroke and the larger overhead
camshaft machines, the 250cc
MOV was to be the ancestor of a
series of overhead valve machines
that culminated in the 500cc
Thruxton.*

**1934 Velocette KTS
Motorcycle.
£4,000-5,000** *HOLL*

**1937 Velocette GTP 250cc
Motorcycle,** fully restored.
Est. £2,200-2,400 *S*

**1959 Velocette Venom 500cc
Motorcycle,** overhead valve.
£4,400-4,800 *VER*

**1959 Velocette Venom 500cc
Motorcycle,** good condition.
Est. £2,750-3,150 *S*

**1953 Velocette LE 200cc
Motorcycle.
£400-500** *S*

1959 Velocette Viper Clubman's 350cc Motorcycle.
£2,000-2,500 *S*

1959 Velocette Venom 500cc Clubman's Motorcycle.
£2,500-3,000 *S*

The Venom, in common with Velocette's other large singles, was a high camshaft overhead valve model, offered in 36 and 38bhp and popular in Clubman racing.

1968 Velocette Thruxton 500cc Motorcycle, good condition.
Est. £8,000-9,500 *S*

Developed from the Venom, the Thruxton was Velocette's answer to the declining sales of their single cylinder 500s. Featuring a large valve head, and Amal GP carburettor, the machines produced a claimed 41bhp, and were to prove popular with both fast road riders and racers.

1968 Velocette LE 192cc Motorcycle.
£500-1,500 *LVC*

Introduced in 1948 featuring a hand starter and hand gear lever, LE or 'Little Engine' initially found favour with police forces, thanks to its almost silent running. Development saw the adoption of a foot operated gearbox and kickstart in 1959 having already grown in capacity to 192cc in 1951.

1955 Velocette LE 192cc Motorcycle.
£500-1,000 *LVC*

VINCENT

1949 Vincent Rapide 1000cc Rapide Series C Motorcycle, Lucas lighting and dynamo, Norton clutch, coil ignition, Amal monobloc carburettors.
Est. £9,500-11,500 *P*

1950 Vincent Rapide 1000cc Series C Motorcycle, fully restored.
Est. £9,000-10,000 *S*

Philip Vincent's first 1000cc twin appeared in 1936 and its quality, performance and handling took the motorcycle world by storm. The post war Rapides were progressively developed culminating in the Series C which was produced from 1948 to 1954.

1951 Vincent Rapide
1000cc Motorcycle.
£8,000-10,000 *VER*

1953 Vincent Black Shadow
1000cc Motorcycle.
£12,000-15,000 *PC*

1951 Vincent Comet 500cc
Motorcycle.
Est. £3,500-4,000 *S*

Locate the Source

*The source of each
illustration in Miller's
can be found by checking
the code letters below
each caption with the
key to illustrations.*

1952 Vincent Rapide 1000cc
Series C Motorcycle.
£17,500-18,500 *CM*

*This motorcycle was bought in
1962 and was delivered in 5
cardboard boxes. Every moving
part has been replaced and
completely rebuilt, the machine
has since travelled only 360 miles.
Was 'Bike of Show' in Bristol
1991.*

Vincent Rapide 1000cc Series
C Motorcycle.
Est. £7,500-8,800 *P*

VINDEC

1926 Vindec 300cc Motorcycle, restored to concours standard.
£2,000-4,000 *TE*

Only the original engine, gearbox and basic frame were supplied to restorers. All other parts manufactured, including most of the internal mechanical parts.

YAMAHA

1964 Yamaha YDS 2 250cc Motorcycle.
£1,500-1,800 *S*

WSK

1972 WSK 175cc Motorcycle, single cylinder 2 stroke engine, 4 speed gearbox.
Est. £1,000-1,300 *S*

c1981 Yamaha YZ 495cc Motorcycle.   **£3,000-4,000** *S*

ZENITH

1927 Zenith V Twin 680cc Motorcycle.
£6,500-7,500 *VER*

ZUNDAPP

1958 Zundapp 200S Motorcycle, fair condition.
Est. £300-450 *S*

Introduced in 1955 the Zundapp 200s featured a 197cc single cylinder 2 stroke with bore and stroke of 64 x 62mm, 12bhp at 5400rpm, and a claimed top speed of 62.5mph. The cycle parts followed contemporary West German practice featuring full mudguards, a spine frame and Earles front forks.

COMPETITION MOTORCYCLES
AERMACCHI

1962 Aermacchi Racer 350cc Motorcycle.
£3,400-3,600 *VER*

1964 Aermacchi 250cc Ala D'Oro Racing Motorcycle, short stroke engine, 72 x 61mm, good condition.
Est. £9,000-10,000 *S*

Aermacchi's elegant Ala d'Oro 250 and 350 4 stroke single met with considerable success throughout the 1960s in national racing, with factory development and tuning work carried out by sponsors and owners helping the machines to match the performance of the increasingly numerous 2 strokes. However, by the 70's the 2 strokes had found much of the reliability that had been lacking and started to dominate racing at all levels.

AJS

1950 AJS 350cc Model 16 Replica Trials Motorcycle, bore and stroke 69 x 93mm, 348cc, compression ratio 6.3 overhead valve, single cylinder, wheel base 54in, ground clearance 8in (20cm), seat height 31in (79cm), 16bhp, rear tyre 18in x 4.00, front 21in.
£1,800-2,200 *P*

1961 AJS 7R 350cc Racing Motorcycle.
£18,500-20,000 *S*

1949/50 AJS 7R 350cc Racing Motorcycle. Est. £10,000-11,000 *S*

ARIEL

Ariel 350cc Racing Motorcycle.
£600-800 *S*

BSA

c1949 BSA B34 Trials 500cc Motorcycle.
Est. £1,100-1,400 *S*

BSA placed great emphasis on off-road sport, especially trials as a way of promoting their products and demonstrating their reliability. This resulted in trials variants of both the Gold Star and B series singles being offered.

DUCATI

Ducati 250cc Racing Motorcycle, overhead cam, air-cooled engine, 18in wheels, alloy rims and wire spokes on Gremeca hubs, telescopic forks, swing and rear suspension, with twin shock absorbers.
Est. £1,800-2,200 *P*

FB/MONDIAL

1955 FB/Mondial 125cc Bialbero Racing Motorcycle.
Est. £14,000-16,000 *S*

From modest beginnings before WWII as manufacturers of delivery 3 wheelers, Fratelli Boselli of Corso Vercelli, Milan, moved their attention to motorcycle manufacture, their first machines being lightweight 2 strokes and a sporting 200cc overhead cam engined machine.

FRANCIS BARNETT

1960 Francis Barnett TS Model M/C 82 25C Trials Motorcycle.
Est. £1,350-1,750 *P*

GREEVES

1959 Greeves Model 24SAS Hawkstone Scrambler Motorcycle, Villiers 250cc 4 speed 2 stroke engine, special alloy square finned barrel and open megaphone exhaust, leading link front forks with 21in (53cm) wheel, swinging arm rear suspension with 19in (48cm) wheel, paddle wheel finned drum brakes, in full running order and restored to show condition.
£1,250-1,500 *PC*

ITOM

1952 Itom 49cc Racing
Motorcycle.
£350-450 *S*

LAVERDA

1971 Laverda 750 SFC Racing
Motorcycle.
Est. £8,000-9,000 *S*

*From modest beginnings as an
extension of the Italian
agricultural equipment business,
the Laverda organisation initially
offered small engined bikes but it
was the 750cc machines
introduced in the late sixties
which established the name in the
big bike market.
The vertical twin cylinder engine
of the 750 initially developed
52bhp at 6900rpm but was
progressively developed until the
750 SFC produced some 70bhp at
7300rpm, making it a serious
competitor on the track.*

MASERATI

c1952 Maserati SS50
Motorcycle.
Est. £2,000-2,400 *BKS*

JAWA

c1980 Jawa DT 500cc Union
Jack Anniversary Speedway
Motorcycle.
Est. £1,000-1,200 *S*

*Designed completely for speedway
competitions, thus brakeless, and
following general speedway
configuration.
This example features the
Czechoslovakian produced Jawa
500cc 4 stroke single engine that
dominated in speedway after the
closure of the British JAP engine
firm.*

MAICO

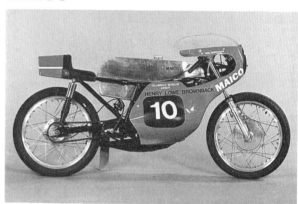

1975 Maico RS 125 R 125cc
Racing Motorcycle.
£2,300-2,500 *S*

*Maico commenced business in
1932, and always concentrated on
smaller machines up to 250cc,
with their own engines (2 strokes
from 125cc to 350cc) after 1945.
The company enjoyed great
success in trials and moto-cross
events, and had a highly
organised racing department.
The company won the World
Manufacturers' Championship in
1973.*

MATCHLESS

1963 Matchless G80 CS 500cc Scramble Motorcycle.
£3,200-3,600 *S*

Sold as the Marksman for the 1963 model year, the Plumstead factory's G80 CS model enjoyed a long production run and considerable popularity for trials and scambles work.

NORTON

1928 Norton CS1 500cc Motorcycle.
£4,300-4,800 *S*

c1949 Norton Model 30 International 490cc Motorcycle.
£4,000-6,000 *S*

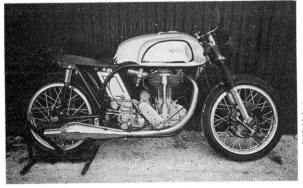

1956 Norton Manx/International 499cc Motorcycle.
Est. £8,000-10,000 *S*

1962 Matchless 650cc Motorcycle.
Est. £16,000-17,000 *S*

MOTO PARILLA

1947 Moto Parilla 250 Grand Prix Racing Motorcycle.
Est. £10,000-11,000 *S*

1944 Norton Manx Garden Gate Motorcycle.
Est. £11,000-13,000 *S*

Arguably the most successful racing machine in history, the Manx Norton has won innumerable victories throughout the world in both private hands and those of the factory riders and, despite its almost vintage engine dimensions, was able to compete successfully with the multi-cylinder machines of first Italy then Japan.

**1956 Norton 30M 490cc
Motorcycle.
£10,000-14,000** *PC*

*Produced in very small numbers
for Grand Prix racing.*

**1958 Norton Manx 40M 350cc
Motorcycle,** overhead valve.
£10,000-11,000 *VER*

**1961 Norton Manx 500cc
Racing Motorcycle.
£18,000-20,000** *S*

Norton Manx Special 500cc,
restored.
£5,000-6,000 *P*

RICKMAN

**1973 Rickman 750cc Racing
Motorcycle.
Est. £3,000-3,500** *S*

ROYAL ENFIELD

**c1933 Royal Enfield Model LF
500cc Trials Motorcycle.
Est. £1,200-1,500** *S*

**1953 Royal Enfield 1 Bullet
Scrambler Motorcycle.
Est. £1,800-2,200** *S*

*The Royal Enfield Bullet met with
considerable success as a trials
model but was also listed in road
racing and scrambler forms.*

**1961 Royal Enfield 248cc
Trials Motorcycle.
Est. £3,800-4,200** *S*

RUDGE

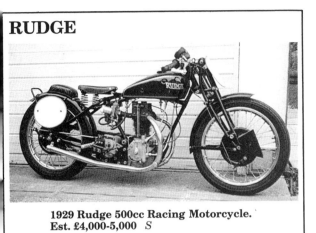

1929 Rudge 500cc Racing Motorcycle.
Est. £4,000-5,000 *S*

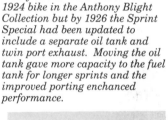

1924 Ex Achille Varzi
Sunbeam Model 9 500cc
Racing Motorcycle.
£7,500-8,500 *S*

This example of the 500cc Model 9, which initially was offered only in competition form is believed to be the earliest surviving example of the Model 9.

SUNBEAM

1926 Sunbeam
Sprint Special
3½hp 500cc
Motorcycle.
£6,000-7,000 *S*

1924 Sunbeam 500cc
Sprint Motorcycle.
£8,000-9,000 *S*

Sunbeam adopted a new Model Number system in 1924 and last in the numbering system was the Model 11 or the 500cc Sprint. The frame design of this all new machine was developed using the experience of ace short distance racer George Dance, a Sunbeam mechanic who was carving out for himself a fine reputation in competition.

A very similar machine to the 1924 bike in the Anthony Blight Collection but by 1926 the Sprint Special had been updated to include a separate oil tank and twin port exhaust. Moving the oil tank gave more capacity to the fuel tank for longer sprints and the improved porting enchanced performance.

1926 Sunbeam Model 9 TT
Replica 500cc Racing
Motorcycle.
£5,000-6,000 *S*

1928 Sunbeam Works Model
90 TT 500cc Racing
Motorcycle.
£13,000-14,000 *S*

1927 Sunbeam Works Model 90
TT 500cc Racing Motorcycle.
£13,000-14,000 *S*

1927 Sunbeam Model 90
TT Replica 500cc
Racing Motorcycle.
£9,000-10,000 *S*

1928 Sunbeam Model 80
Works TT 350cc Racing
Motorcycle.
£7,000-8,000 *S*

1933 Sunbeam
Little 95R 250cc
Racing Motorcycle.
£7,000-8,000 *S*

Sunbeam announced the Little 95 for the 1934 season, curiously using the 95 designation used also for the 500cc bikes, perhaps a marketing ploy. It followed the pattern of its contemporaries with overhead valve engine with hairpin springs and foot change gearbox.

1935 Sunbeam 95R 500cc
Racing Motorcycle.
£5,500-6,000 *S*

SUZUKI

**Suzuki RG500 Solo Racing
Motorcycle.**
£4,000-5,000 *S*

**1979 Suzuki RG500 Mk 5
Racing Motorcycle.**
Est. £7,000-8,000 *S*

*Suzuki's RG500 square four
epitomises the Grand Prix
machine of the 1970s when engine
technology seemed to be forever
two steps in front of tyre and
frame technology.*

**Suzuki RG500
Mark 3
2 Stroke.
Est.
£6,000-6,500** *P*

TRIUMPH

**1935 Triumph L2/1 249cc
Motorcycle.**
Est. £3,000-4,000 *S*

**1966 Triumph Bonneville
Thruxton T120 650cc
Motorcycle.**
Est. £14,000-16,000 *S*

VINCENT

**1949 Vincent Grey Flash, The
Eppynt Racer,** single cylinder,
499cc.
£16,500-17,500 *COYS*

YAMAHA

**c1970 250cc
Yamaha Racing
Motorcycle.**
£200-400 *S*

**c1970s Yamaha YZ Model
250cc Racing Motorcycle,**
Yamaha YZ engine in a
monoshock frame, full race
fairings, Belly Pan etc, Showa
forks, Borrani rims and disc front
brakes with finned drum YD type
brakes at the rear.
Est. £700-800 *S*

MILITARY MOTORCYCLES
BMW

1943 BMW R75 746cc Military Motorcycle Combination, with Steib sidecar.
Est. £3,750-5,000 *S*

Featuring BMW's traditional transverse horizontally opposed twin cylinder engine, overhead valves, and with shaft final drive, the R75 combination was available in a variety of specifications and was a formidable fighting vehicle. Like the contemporary Zündapp KS750, the R75 was specially used as a solo machine. This example features a pillion seat, fitted pannier boxes, and spare wheel mounted on the Steib sidecar.

BSA

1968 BSA B40 WD 350cc Motorcycle.
Est. £800-1,200 *S*

Although sharing many similarities with the civilian B40, the military machine was specially developed by BSA to meet MoD requirements.

c1968 BSA B40 350cc Ex WD Military Motorcycle, good condition.
Est. £600-650 *S*

CAN-AM

1980 Can-Am 250cc Bombardier ex-British Army Solo Motorcycle, Rotax 250cc 2 stroke 5 speed engine/gearbox unit, telescopic front forks with 19in wheel, swinging arm rear suspension with 18 inch wheel, drum brakes, restored to show condition and in running order, with full military equipment.
£650-800 *PC*

COSSACK

c1975 Cossack Model M66 Motorcycle and Sidecar, rear pannier, masked headlamp, single seater sidecar with spare wheel and pillion saddle frame.
£600-800 *S*

HARLEY-DAVIDSON

1949 Harley-Davidson WLA 45 750cc Military Motorcycle.
Est. £3,500-4,000 *S*

Harley-Davidson's 45 cubic inch WLA saw extensive use with all the allied forces during WWII, and was produced in both America and Canada (as the WLC).

1942 Harley-Davidson WLA Military Police Motorcycle.
£3,800-4,300 *S*

Some 88,000 Harley-Davidson motorcycles were produced during WWII and it was the WL model which perhaps most enhanced the company's reputation. Its V-twin L-head engine gave it 65mph performance and 35mpg economy.

INDIAN

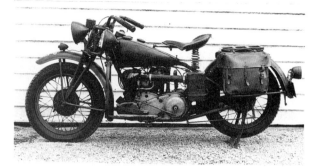

1942 Indian Model 741A Military Motorcycle.
£3,700-4,000 *S*

The 640 was the first of Indian's wartime V-twin bikes, followed by Model 741 and 741A, a low compression slogging side valve machine with girder fork front suspension and rigid rear.

MATCHLESS

1926 Matchless Model M 591cc Motorcycle.
£4,800-5,200 *AMOC*

JAMES

1943 James ML 125cc Motorcycle, single cylinder, 2 stroke, Villiers 9D engine.
£800-1,200 *MVT*

Slightly heavier and more powerful than Royal Enfield's WD/RE and also rarer in military form, there are 2 versions: one with long and the other with short mudguards. Production continued after WWII with only minor changes. The military versions can be identified by the frame numbers ML8500 and under. ML8501 to ML10,000 were ordered but not delivered. All frame numbers following these were used for civilian motorcycles. Parts availability is fair.

1924 Matchless L/3 350cc Motorcycle.
£3,000-4,000 *VMCC*

1941 Matchless G3L 350cc Military Motorcycle.
£1,000-1,500 *S*

With the outbreak of war in 1939 Matchless produced the overhead valve 350cc Model G3 for despatch rider use. For greater service reliability a lower compression engine was adopted and a rear carrier rack with 2 canvas panniers was fitted. From 1941 the G3 became the G3L with the introduction of teledraulic forks, a landmark feature in British motorcycle design, inspired by the demands of war.

MOTO-GUZZI

**c1945/6 Moto-Guzzi Super Alce
500cc Military Motorcycle,**
unspoilt original condition.
£1,400-1,800 *S*

*Superseding the legendary Moto-
Guzzi Alce (Elk) (which was itself
developed from the GT20 model),
the Super Alce was Italian built
and like its predecessors, designed
specifically for use by the Italian
military.*

ROYAL ENFIELD

**1940 Royal Enfield 'Flying
Flea' Model RE Motorcycle,**
working order.
£450-650 *S*

**1943 Royal Enfield WD/CO
350cc Motorcycle,** overhead
valve.
£1,000-1,400 *MVT*

MV AGUSTA

**1975 MV Agusta 350GT 350cc
Police Motorcycle.**
£700-1,000 *S*

NSU

**c1942 NSU HK101
Kettenkraftrad Tracked
Motorcycle.**
£5,000-6,000 *S*

*NSU and Stoewer produced this
semi-tracked motorcycle from
1940-1944 which could
accommodate a driver and 2
passengers who faced rearwards
and it was also known as the
Kettenkrad for short. The engine
was a 4 cylinder Opel Olympia
1,500cc unit mounted behind the
driver and there was a 3 speed
gearbox and 2 speed auxilliary
box. They were capable of towing
a trailer or Pak anti-tank guns.*

ZUNDAPP

**1943 Zundapp KS 750cc
Motorcycle,** V-twin (170°),
overhead valve. **£4,500-6,000** *MVT*

*The motorcycle has shaft drive,
permanent 2 wheel drive through
a differential (with a differential
lock) and reverse gear. It is similar
in layout to BMW's R75 with whom
it shares some components, for
instance the rear hub, wheels,
sidecar body and chassis (later
versions only). Most parts are
available in reproduction form
from Germany but are very expensive.*

BICYCLES

An Acrobatic Bicycle.
£60-80 *S*

An Udaila Bicycle.
£170-190 *S*

This Japanese cycle with double lateral frame was recently displayed as part of the multiple element section of the Transport Design and Development Museum at Kew.

Manufactured by the German engineering company equally famous for motor car and typewriter manufacture.

1930s Adler Ladies Loop Framed Bicycle.
£260-300 *S*

Three Humber Bicycles.
Est. £100-150 *S*

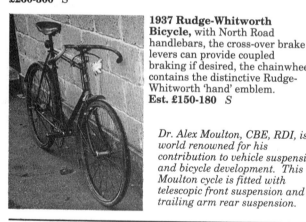

1937 Rudge-Whitworth Bicycle, with North Road handlebars, the cross-over brake levers can provide coupled braking if desired, the chainwheel contains the distinctive Rudge-Whitworth 'hand' emblem.
Est. £150-180 *S*

Dr. Alex Moulton, CBE, RDI, is world renowned for his contribution to vehicle suspension and bicycle development. This Moulton cycle is fitted with telescopic front suspension and trailing arm rear suspension.

1964 Moulton Stowaway Bicycle.
£200-220 *S*

MOTORISED BICYCLES & AUTOCYCLES

1955 Alcyon Autocycle.
£450-550 *S*

The Alcyon company started production in 1902, and in the post-war years concentrated on machines up to 248cc in capacity.

1968 Clark Scamp 49cc Autocycle.
£250-350 *S*

Produced in the Isle of Wight in very limited numbers by A.N. Clark, this is believed to be one of 4 Scamps in existence.

1950 Le Poulan Cycle Motor.
£250-350 *S*

**1956 Cyclemaster 32cc
Butcher's Trade Motor
Assisted Pedal Cycle.
Est. £700-900 *S***

*Most successful of a plethora of
motor attachments designed to
convert a pedal cycle into a
motorised bicycle, the Cyclemaster
was a neat design in which the
engine was located within the rear
wheel.*

A James Autocycle, underslung
fuel tank, curved frame top tube,
traditional James maroon
paintwork and original transfers.
Est. £200-220 *S*

**A Magpi Electric Shopping
Bicycle,** with friction drive, 2
panniers on either side of the rear
wheel contain 2 batteries, with a
'trigger' on the handlebar
controlling the motor. The cycle
parts of conventional dropped
frame shopping design, with a 3
speed rear hub and chromium
mudguards.
£200-300 *S*

**1957 New Hudson 98cc
Re-styled Model Autocycle.**
£200-400 *NAC*

*New Hudson ceased production
after a couple of years as it proved
not to be competitive.*

c1974 Solex S3800 Autocycle.
£150-250 *S*

*An original example of the
popular French built Solex
Autocycle with forward mounted,
single cylinder, air-cooled, 2 stroke
engine driving by friction roller to
the front wheel. The machine is
pedal assisted and complete with
luggage carrier and 0-40mph
speedometer.*

A Rayral Autocycle.
£150-180 *S*

*This autocycle was produced
before and after WWII.*

TRICYCLES

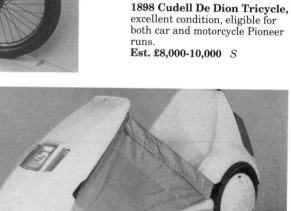

1898 Cudell De Dion Tricycle, excellent condition, eligible for both car and motorcycle Pioneer runs.
Est. £8,000-10,000 *S*

1898 Dennis Speed King Autocycle, 2½hp.
£14,000-16,000 *VER*

Typical of the tricycles that were popular at the turn of the century, this machine would be eligible for both the motorcycle and the car Pioneer Runs to Brighton.

1971 Ariel 3 Moped Tricycle.
Est. £400-500 *LF*

1985 Sinclair C5 Electric Tricycle.
£250-350 *S*

MOPEDS & SCOOTERS

1974 Puch 50cc Moped, 3 speed gearbox, pillion seat and luggage carrier.
£150-250 *S*

Two Raleigh Mopeds. Est. £100-120 *S*

Motobecane Mobyx. **£150-170** *S*

1957 Lambretta Model D Motor Scooter, 150cc 2 stroke engine, pillion seat, luggage box, lighting and electric horn.
£700-1,000 *S*

**1970s Hewitt Prototype
Electric Motorcycle.
£550-650** *S*

**1977 NVT Easy Rider 49cc
Moped.
£150-250** *S*

*In an attempt to increase their
market share, the Norton Villiers
Triumph group diversified into
the production of lightweight 2
strokes in the latter part of the 70s
with 2 trial bikes (125cc and
175cc) and a series of mopeds.
Offered in sporting and step-three
styles, the mopeds followed
conventional practices, although
the use of a single large diameter
tube as the main frame members
was unusual.*

**c1960 The 'Scorge Special'
Moped.
£30-60** *S*

*Based on an NSU Quickly moped,
this machine has been modified
for grass track racing, and
features a pair of band type forks,
knobbly tyres and lowered right
footrest, of the hook type to assist
broadsliding.*

**1919 ABC Scootamota.
£1,500-2,000** *S*

**Corgi Scooter.
£500-600** *S*

*Colonel Dolphin of Welwyn
designed the very basic Welbike to
fit in a cylindrical container and
to be dropped as support transport
for the paratroops. The Welbike
adopted a Villiers Junior 98cc 2
stroke engine, collapsible steering
column and handlebars and had
twin pannier fuel tanks astride
the frame. The Welbike was
produced by Excelsior who were to
design the Excelsior Spryt engine
which was to power the post-war
civilian Corgi Scooter.
Brockhouse built the Spryt engine
under licence and their Corgi
shared many of the Welbike's
folding characteristics.*

**1953 Corgi 98cc Motor
Scooter.
£250-350** *S*

c1948 Brockhouse Corgi 98cc Scooter, Excelsior Spryt 2 stroke engine.
£200-300 *S*

1982 Suzuki FZ50 50cc Motorcycle, automatic gearbox, full weather protection, front luggage basket, rear carrier, and windshield.
£150-200 *S*

The 1980s saw the traditional moped giving way to machines of the scooter type.

1919 ABC Scootamota 124cc Motor Scooter, rear mounted four stroke engine.
£350-550 *S*

1962 Capri 80cc Motor Scooter.
£300-400 *S*

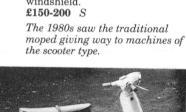

1953 Lambretta 125cc Motor Scooter.
£700-1,000 *S*

1957 Durkopp Diana Sport 194cc Motor Scooter, 2 stroke, single cylinder engine, 4 speed gearbox, handlebar mounted headlamp, higher compression ratio, more performance orientated porting, fair original condition.
£200-300 *S*

Velo Solex 49cc Moped.
£60-100 *S*

These machines relied on a front mounted single cylinder 2 stroke engine, driving the front wheel by direct friction drive, whilst the rest of the machine followed bicycle practice in a more robust form.

Maicoletta 250cc Scooter, 300 x 14in wheels, an oscillating, electric starter.
£1,500-1,700 *MOC*

CYCLE MEMORABILIA
Art

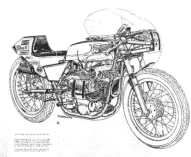

B. S. Smith, Norton John Player Special 750 Daytona 1972, pen and ink cut-away drawing, signed, published by Motor Cycle Magazine, 15¾ x 22in (40 x 56cm), framed and glazed.
£100-200 *S*

***Burton,** Shell Hill Climb Team, colour lithograph, 1926, printed by Waterlow & Sons, 30 x 45in (76 x 114cm).
£450-550 *P*

HK, Plunger Manx Norton, limited edition print 12/64, initialled, 12½ x 19in (31.5 x 48cm), mounted, framed and glazed.
£20-30 *S*

Geo. Ham, Motorcyclist, print, 17 x 23½in (43 x 60cm), framed and glazed.
£80-100 *S*

Gordon Horner, Derek Minter on the Manx Norton, Isle of Man Tourist Trophy 1961, monochrome watercolour with wash, commissioned for The Motor Cycle, depicting Minter finishing the hard way, signed and dated 1961, paper creased, 21 x 29in (53.5 x 73.5cm), mounted framed and glazed.
£450-650 *S*

Gordon Horner, German World Championship Sidecar Grand Prix 1965, depicting the Works BMW's cornering hard, monochrome watercolour with wash, commissioned for The Motor Cycle, with date stamp, signed, 12½ x 29in (32.5 x 73.5cm), mounted, framed and glazed.
£300-400 *S*

Phil May, 1950 Isle of Man TT, watercolour depicting 2 Norton riders at speed, signed, 11½ x 14½in (29 x 37cm), framed and glazed.
Est. £150-180 *S*

Rod Organ, Hero's Return, limited edition print, number 63/950, depicting Mike Hailwood on a Ducati, 13 x 20½in (33 x 52cm), framed and glazed.
£75-100 *S*

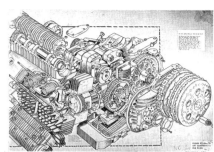

Richie, AJS 1947 Works Parallel Twin Racing Engine, pen and ink cut-away drawing, published by Motor Cycle Magazine, signed, dated, 20½ x 29½in (52 x 75cm), framed and glazed.
£100-250 *S*

Clothing

Three pairs of motorists' goggles:
l. Triplex Aero and Motor Goggles, c1920s.
c. Uvex motor/aviation goggles, c1940s.
r. Early motorist's face masking goggles, c1912.
£120-170 each *BKS*

Gordon Horner, A Manx Norton Racing a Sports Car, monochrome watercolour with wash, commissioned by The Castrol Oil Company, paper creased, 11 x 25in (28 x 63.5cm), mounted, framed and glazed.
£300-400 *S*

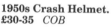

1950s Crash Helmet.
£30-35 *COB*

A pair of Edwardian motorist's goggles, in original leatherette carrying case, c1910.
£90-120 *BKS*

1960s Crash Helmet, with original box.
£30-35 *COB*

Ephemera -
MAGAZINES

The Motor Cycle, 1966, 4 volumes with covers and advertisements, with indices.
£170-200 *S*

Motor Cycling, 1925-1961, assorted loose issues, majority post-1945.
£70-100 *S*

Miller's is a price GUIDE not a price LIST

Classic Bike, 1978-1982, the first 3 bound volumes.
Est. £180-250 *S*

The Motor Cycle, 1926-1943, assorted loose issues from the period, approximately 158, variable condition.
£150-200 *S*

PROGRAMMES

Two Speedway programmes, 1939.
£10-15 each *COB*

Motor Cycle and Grand Prix Programmes, 1937, 1938 and 1939.
£15-20 each *COB*

A collection of sales catalogues and magazines, including catalogues for James and Norton, spare parts lists for Douglas and Triumph and other ephemera.
£80-100 *S*

Motor Cycling, 1927, one bound volume, July to December, including show issues.
£90-120 *S*

A 1930s Motor Cycling programme.
£15-20 *COB*

1935 Wembley Speedway programme.
£10-15 *COB*

POSTERS

Triumph 1971 Year of the Big Wins Poster, depicting Percy Tate, 25½ x 35in (65 x 89cm), framed and glazed.
£50-70 *S*

A Matchless advertisement, Spring Song By Matchless, depicting G80s, framed and glazed, together with a similiar advertisement for Ariel, 17½ x 12in (44.5 x 31cm). **£50-100** *S*

MISCELLANEOUS

A Collection of sales catalogues and leaflets, 1932 to 1936. **£60-140 each** *S*

A Set of 50 cigarette cards, Lambert and Butler Motorcycles, 1923, in double-sided glazed frame.
£100-150 *S*

Seventeen Motorcycling books, including R.W. Burgess, J. R. Clew and John Griffith.
£70-110 *S*

MOTORCYCLE PARTS

Three Brough Superior sales brochures, for 1937, 1938 and 1939, 1938 lacking rear cover.
£190-230 *S*

A Norton Model 7 petrol tank, 1950, together with a Norton Oil tank, restored.
£100-120 *S*

A Norton 500cc cylinder head, together with 8 hairspring valve springs from a racing Manx Norton or KTT Velocette, with other spares. **£60-80** *S*

A Honda dual seat, and other miscellaneous items.
£70-100 *S*

SIGNS

A Queen's Award to Industry sign, found in a cupboard on the day the Triumph factory closed, 25th August 1983. **Priceless** *CM*

A Matchless agents' illuminated motorcycle sign.
£60-65 *COB*

MISCELLANEOUS

A Triumph factory nameplate.
Priceless *CM*

A 1950s plastic motorcycle, made in the U.S.A.
£30-40 *COB*

MOTORCYCLE CLUBS DIRECTORY

If you wish to be included in next year's directory or if you have a change of address or telephone number, please could you inform us by April 30th 1994. Entries will be repeated in subsequent editions unless we are requested otherwise.

AJS & Matchless Owners Club, 25 Bevington Close,Patchway, Bristol, Avon

AMC Owners Club, C/o Terry Corley, 12 Chilworth Gardens, Sutton, Surrey

Androd Classics, 70 Broadway, Frome, Somerset
Tel: 0373 471087

Ariel Owners Club, C/o Mike Taylor, Harrow House, Woolscott, Rugby, Warwicks

Bantam Enthusiasts Club, C/o Vic Salmon, 16 Oakhurst Close, Walderslade, Chatham, Kent

Benelli Owners Club, C/o Rosie Marston, 14 Rufford Close, Barton Seagrave, Kettering, Northants

BMW Owners Club, C/o Mike Cox, 22 Combermere, Thornbury, Bristol

Bristol & Avon Roadrunners, 177 Speedwell Road, Speedwell, Bristol
Tel: 0831 851728

Bristol & District Sidecar Club, 158 Fairlyn Drive, Kingswood, Bristol, Avon

Bristol Genesis Motorcycle Club, Burrington, 1a Bampton Close, Headley Park, Bristol
Tel: 0272 782584

Bristol Micro Car Club, 123 Queens Road, Bishopsworth, Bristol
Tel: 0272 642901

British Two Stroke Owners Club, C/o Mark Hathaway, 45 Moores Hill, Olney, Bucks

British Motorcyclists Federation, 129 Seaforth Avenue, Motspur Park, New Malden, Surrey

British Motor Bike Owners, C/o Ray Peacock, Crown Inn, Shelfanger, Diss, Norfolk

British Motorcycle Owners, C/o Phil Coventry, 59 Mackenzie Street, Bolton

Brough Superior Club, C/o Piers Otley, 6 Canning Road, Felpham, West Sussex

BSA Owners Club, C/o Rob Jones, 44 Froxfield Road, West Leigh, Havant, Hants

CBX Riders Club, C/o Peter Broad, 57 Osborne Close, Basingstoke, Hampshire

Christian Motorcyclists Association, PO Box 113, Wokingham, Berkshire

Cossack Owners Club, C/o Dorothy Noble, 67 Charnock, Skelmersdale, Lancs

DKW Rotary Owners Club, C/o David Cameron, Dunbar, Ingatestone Road, Highwood, Chelmsford Essex

Douglas Owners Club, C/o Reg Holmes, 48 Standish Avenue, Stoke Lodge, Patchway, Bristol, Avon

Ducati Owners Club, 131 Desmond Drive, Old Catton, Norwich

Dunstall Owners Club, C/o Barry Hutchinson, PO Box 51, Prestwich, Manchester

Featherbed Specials Owners Club, Curteif Farm, Lower Road, Tenterden, Kent

Francis Barnett Owners Club, 58 Knowle Road, Totterdown, Bristol

Gold Star Owners Club, C/o Brian Shackleford, 88 Hykham Road, Lincoln

Goldwing Owners Club GB, 82 Farley Close, Little Stoke, Bristol

Greeves Owners Club, C/o Dave McGregor, 4 Longshaw Close, North Wingfield, Chesterfield, Derbyshire

Greeves Riders Association, 40 Swallow Park, Thornbury, Avon
Tel: 0454 418037

Harley Davidson Owners Club, 1 St Johns Road, Clifton, Bristol

Harley Davidson Riders Club of Great Britain, Membership Secretary, PO Box 62, Newton Abbott, Devon

Hesketh Owners Club, C/o Peter White, 1 Northfield Road, Soham, Cambs

Honda Owners Club, C/o Dave Barton, 18a Embley Close, Calmore, Southampton

Indian Motorcycle Club GB, Surrey Mills, Chilworth, Guildford, Surrey

International CBX Owners Association, 24 Pevensey Way, Paddock Hill, Frimley, Camberley, Surrey
Tel: 0252 836698

International Laverda Owners Club, C/o Alan Cudipp, Orchard Cottage, Orchard Terrace, Acomb, Hexham, Northumberland

Italian Motorcycle Owners Club, C/o Rosie Marston, 14 Rufford Close, Barton Seagrave, Kettering

Jawa-CZ Owners MCC, C/o Peter Edwards, 2 Churchill Close, Breaston, Derbyshire

Kawasaki Owners Club, C/o John Dalton, 37 Hinton Road, Runcorn, Cheshire

Laverda Owners Club, C/o Dick Hutton, 78 Rufford Rise, Sothall, Sheffield

Le Velocette Club, 32 Mackie Avenue, Filton, Bristol, Avon

L E Velo Club, C/o Peter Greaves, 8 Heath Close, Walsall, West Midlands

Maico Owners Club, C/o Phil Hingston, No Elms, Goosey, Nr Faringdon, Oxon

Military Vehicle Trust, 3 The Birches, West Pontnewydd, Cwmbran, Gwent

Morini Owners Club, C/o Richard Laughton, 20 Fairford Close, Church Hill, Redditch, Worcs

Morini Riders Club, 3 Minden Close, Wokingham, Surrey
Tel: 0734 793362

Moto Guzzi Club GB, C/o Jenny Trengove, 53 Torbay Road, Harrow, Middlesex

MV Agusta Club GB, C/o Martyn Simpkins, 31 Baker Street, Stapenhill, Burton-on-Trent

MZ Riders Club, Lychgate Cottage, Church St North, Liskeard, Cornwall
Tel: 0579 342582

National Autocycle & Cyclemotor Club, C/o D Butler, 20 Bromford Hill, Handsworth Wood, Birmingham

National Hill Climb Association, 43 Tyler Close, Hanham, Bristol
Tel: 0272 443569

New Imperial Owners Association, C/o Mike Slater, 3 Fairview Drive, Higham, Kent

North Devon British Motorcycle Owners Club, Bassett Lodge, Pollards Hill, Torrington, North Devon

Norton Owners Club, C/o Dave Fenner, Beeches, Durley Brook Road, Durley, Southampton

North Wilts British Motorcycle Club, 20 St Philips Road, Stratton St Margaret, Swindon, Wilts

Norton Owners Club, 47 Pendennis Park, Brislington, Bristol
Tel: 0272 772985

Panther Owners Club, C/o A & J Jones, Coopers Cottage, Park Lane, Castle Camps, Cambridge

Raleigh Safety Seven and Early Reliant Owners Club, 26 Victoria Road, Southwick, Sussex

Rickman Owners Club, C/o Michael Foulds, 35 Otterbourne Road, Chingford, London E4

Royal Enfield Owners Club, C/o John Cherry, Meadow Lodge Farm, Henfield, Coalpit, Heath, Bristol

Rudge Enthusiasts Club, C/o Sue Jackson-Scott, 117 Church Lane, Chessington, Surrey

Scott Owners Club, C/o H Beal, 2 Whiteshott, Basildon, Essex

Shrivenham Motorcycle Club, 12-14 Townsend Road, Shrivenham, Swindon, Wilts

Street Specials Motorcycle Club, C/o E Warrington, 8 The Gallops, Norton, Malton, North Yorkshire

Sunbeam Owners Club, C/o Stewart Engineering, Church Terrace, Harbury, Leamington Spa, Warwickshire

Sunbeam Owners Fellowship, PO Box 7, Market Harborough, Leicestershire

Suzuki Owners Club, C/o Ken Fulton, Wentworth Crescent, Hayes, Middlesex

The Sidecar Register, C/o John Proctor, 112 Briarlyn Road, Birchencliffe, Huddersfield

Trident and Rocket Three Owners Club, 63 Dunbar Road, Southport, Merseyside

Triumph Motorcycle Club, 6 Hortham Lane, Almondsbury, Bristol, Avon

Triumph Owners Club, C/o Mrs M Mellish, 4 Douglas Avenue, Harold Wood, Romford, Essex

Velocette Owners Club, C/o Vic Blackman, 1 Mayfair, Tilehurst, Reading, Berks

Vincent Owners Club, C/o John Kinley, The Old Manse, High Road, Wortwell, Harlestone, Norfolk

Vintage Japanese MCC, C/o John Dalton, 1 Maple Avenue, Burchill, Onchan, Isle of Man

Vintage Motor Cycle Club, Allen House, Wetmore Road, Burton-on-Trent, Staffordshire
Tel: 0283 40557

Vintage Motorcycle Club of Ulster, C/o Mrs M Burns, 20 Coach Road, Comber, Newtownards, Co Down

Vintage Motor Scooter Club, 11 Ivanhoe Avenue, Lowton St Lukes, Nr Warrington, Cheshire

Vintage Japanese Motorcycle Club, 9 Somerset Crescent, Melksham, Wilts
Tel: 0225 702816

ZI Owners Club, C/o Sam Holt, 54 Hawhome Close, Congleton, Cheshire

AJS & Matchless. The Postwar Models. Bacon. Covers the lightweight & heavyweight singles & twins from 1945. Marque history plus data on models. 191 pgs, 179 b&w ill. **£14.95**

Illustrated AJS & Matchless Buyers Guide. Redman. Detailed & fully illustrated review of all models. 160 pgs, 180 b&w ill..**£10.95**

Matchless & AJS Restoration. Bacon. Comprehensive guide to restoration, renovation & development history of all post-war production motorcycles. 304 pgs, 250 photos...**£19.99**

Ariel. The Postwar Models. Bacon. Covers the Square 4, light & heavyweight singles & twins. 192 pgs, 150 b&w ill...........
....**£14.95**

BMW The Complete Story. Preston. History & development of BMW motorcycles with a detailed study of the most important models. 160 pgs, 105 b&w ill. **£14.99**

Illustrated BMW Buyers Guide. Knittel & Slabon. Covers every BMW model from 1923 to current models. 160 pgs, 150 b&w photos...**£10.95**

Classic Motorcycles. BMW. Morley & Woollett. All the favourite and most important BMWs in superb colour photography. 128 pgs, 120 colour ill. ....
....**£10.99**

BMW Twins Restoration. Walker. Comprehensive guide to restoration, renovation & development history of all BMW flat twins, 1955-1985. 240 pgs, 220 ill.
....**£19.99**

BSA, The Complete Story. Wright. Detailed history of the marque & its models. Photographs & line drawings. Specification table. 160 pgs, 190 b&w ill.................**£15.99**

Illustrated BSA Buyers Guide. Bacon. Model by model analysis of the postwar singles, twins, triples & specials. 160 pgs, 200 ill. **£10.95**

Classic Motorcycles. BSA. Morley. All colour photographs of many BSA models. 128 pgs, 120 colour ill..........................**£10.99**

BSA Gold Star & Other Singles. Bacon. Covers the Gold Star; B,M,C ranges; Bantam & unit singles. 192 pgs, 132 b&w ill..**£14.95**

Classic Motorcycles. Walker. Covers, country by country, over 150 of the world's finest bikes since 1945. Stunning colour photographs. Large format book. 110 pgs...
....**£8.99**

Superbikes. Brown. Road machines of the 60's, 70's, 80's and 90's. Large format book. 112 pgs. Col photos..............................**£8.99**

Classic Motorbikes. Hicks. From invention & innovation to the present & future classics. Large format book. 144 pgs, 270 col. ill. **£9.99**

Phil Irving. Irving. Phil Irving MBE, whose 60 year international career included the design of motorcycles, in particular the Vincent, motor cars & the famous Repco-Brabham Grand Prix engine, tells the fascinating story of his career in innovative auto design. 569 pgs. £24.95

A Man Called Mike. Hilton. A biography of the legendary Mike Hailwood. 256 pgs, b&w & col photos.................................£16.95

The Gold Star Book. BMS. A workshop manual with parts list. 138 pgs, 174 ill........ ....£10.95

BSA Singles Restoration. Bacon. Covers all post-war pre-unit singles including the Gold Star, B, M, & C series plus four strokes & Bantams. 304 pgs, 250 ill...............£19.99

BSA Twin Restoration. Bacon. The essential restoration & renovation guide for all post-war twins. 240 pgs, 270 ill....£19.99

Ducati Tuning. Eke. For all the V-Twins with bevel drive camshafts. 112 pgs, 77 ill. £12.00

Ducati Singles Restoration. Walker. Diagrams, expert text, special techniques & guide to authentic Ducati detailing. 240 pgs, 250 ill. £18.99

Ducati Twins Restoration. Walker. A must for any Ducati twin owner or restorer. 240 pgs, 250 ill. £19.99

Big Book of Harley. Bolfert. The official publication of Harley-Davidson Inc. Traces the history of the company with over 1000 colour photos. 272 pgs, 1200 b&w & colour ill. £35.50

The Classic Harley. Williams. The bikes, their riders & their lifestyles in colour. Superb photos throughout. 144 pgs...£16.99

Harley-Davidson. A Pictorial Celebration. Birkett. The bikes, accessories & official clothing & how they add up to the Harley-Davidson way of life. 160 pgs, colour throughout £16.99

Illustrated Harley-Davidson Buyers Guide. Girdler. Second Ed. Details the models from 1936 to the new 1993 models. 176 pgs, 141 b&w ill. £10.95

Harley-Davidson Sportster Performance Handbook. Buzzelli. Complete guide to improving your Sportster. Traces the evolution of the Sportster from 1957 to today. 192 pgs, 300 b&w ill................£13.95

Tech Tips & Tricks. Vols 1 & 2. How to do it tips. Guides, charts & Harley-Davidson reference material.
Vol 1 ....£7.95
Vol 2 ....£9.95

Honda. The Complete Story. Parker. Traces the company's development through all the major models from 1946 to the superbikes of the 80's & 90's. 160 pgs, 100 ill. £14.99

Classic Motorcycles. Honda. Walker. A history in full colour. 128 pgs. £10.99

Honda. Conquerors of the Track. Hilton. A chronicle of Honda's dominance of world motorcycle racing over the past 30 years. 196 pgs, b&w & colour ill. £15.99

Indian Motorcycles. Kanter. **NEW!** The Indian's history from the early singles & twins to the age of the Scouts, Chiefs, Fours & the classic racers to the end of the line in 1953. 96 pgs, 80 colour photos. £9.95

Laverda Twin & Triples. Parker. Repair & tune up guide. Factory approved. 176 pgs, 294 ill..£21.95

Illustrated Moto Guzzi Buyers Guide. Walker. Model by model analysis of post-war singles, twins & fours. 160 pgs, 180 ill.. ....£10.95

Moto Guzzi (English Ed.) Colombo. Encyclopaedia of Moto Guzzi. The history, technical developments, catalogue of models, specifications and photos. 411 pgs, 552 b&w, 32 colour ill. **£44.95**

M V Agusta. Colombo & Patrignani. A history of the marque with a complete catalogue of production & racing models. English text. 245 pgs, 353 b&w, 20 colour ill. **£39.95**

Norton Illustrated Buyers Guide. Bacon. Information, specifications & technical details on all the models for the enthusiast, owner or potential buyer. 160 pgs, 150 ill. **£10.95**

Norton Service & Overhaul Manual. Neill. Covers the single cylinder 347cc 50, 490cc ES2 & the twin cylinder 250cc Jubilee, 350cc Navigator, 400cc Electra, 497cc 88, 88 de luxe 88SS, 99 Standard, 99SS, 99 De Luxe, 650 Standard, 650 de luxe, 650 America, 650SS, 650 Manxman, 750 Atlas, 750 Scrambler, 750 G15 CS. 176 pgs, 123 ill. **£12.00**

Norton Twin Restoration. Bacon. Guide to the renovation, restoration & development history of all post-war Norton Twins including Commando, Featherbed, Dominator & Jubilee series. 240 pgs, 250 ill. **£19.99**

Classic Motorcycles. Norton. Morley. The fascinating history of the company & the bikes from the beginning to the high powered rotaries. Full colour. 128 pgs, 120 colour ill. **£10.99**

Manx Norton. Walker. Traces the design, development & racing record of the Manx. Superb collection of photographs. 192 pgs, 200 ill. **£17.95**

Norton. Woollett. Follows the development of all Norton motorcycles, racing, off-road & Roadster. A definitive history of the oldest marque in the world. 320 pgs, 250 ill. **£25.00**

Royal Enfield. The Postwar Models. Bacon. The 125, 150, 250, 350, 500, 700, 750 Singles & Twins. Analysis & specifications. **£14.95**

Rumi. Crippa. A model by model history of the bikes. Competition history, specifications & much more. Italian text. 255 pgs, 292 b&w, 16 colour ill. **£44.95**

Don't Trudge It - Rudge It. Reynolds. Brings alive former glory of a great name; a history of this motor cycle from the beginning of the century. 173 pgs, over 100 b&w ill...**£9.95**

Scott Motor Cycle: Yowling Two-Stroke. Clew. The man, the machines, the factory: it's successes and failures, racing results. 239 pgs. **£10.95**

Classic Motorcycles: Suzuki. Walker. Full colour. A history from 1952 to the multi-cylinder models including the liquid-cooled 750's & the RE5. 128 pgs, full colour. **£10.99**

Classic Motorcycles: Triumph. Morley. A history in full colour. 128 pgs. **£10.99**

Triumph: The Complete Story. Davies. From the days of Siegfried Bettmann in 1885 to the relaunch of the Triumph name in 1990. 160 pgs, 100 b&w ill. **£14.99**

Triumph Twins & Triples. Bacon. The 300, 500, 650, 750 Twins & Trident. A history plus specs., colour & recognition. 192 pgs, 165 ill..**£10.95**

Triumph Twin Restoration. Bacon. Comprehenisve restoration guide. 240 pgs, 250 ill. **£19.99**

Velocette: Technical Excellence. Rhodes. History of the machine's development & competition successes plus the story of the people behind the marque. 196 pgs, 180 b&w photos. **£19.99**

Velocette: Viper/Venom/Thruxton. 350 Singles. BMS. Service manual. 64 pgs, 134 ill...**£8.95**

Vespa: An Illustrated History. Brockway. Fascinating collection of photographs. 96 pgs, b&w photos....................................**£9.99**

Triumph Tiger 100 Daytona. Nelson. The development history of pre-unit and unit construction 500cc bikes. Specs, colour schemes. 168 pgs, 232 b&w illus. **£8.95**

Triumph Tuning. Shenton. For the 500 & 650cc twin-cylinder engine and the 750cc three. 54 pgs, b&w ill. **£6.00**

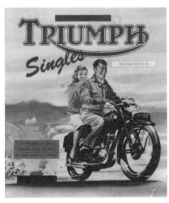

Triumph Singles. Bacon. Late pre-war models incl. Terrier Cub, Trophy, Blazer & scooters. A history plus specs., colours & recognition. 127 pgs, 71 b&w photos, 3 ill.... ....**£13.95**

Villiers: Singles & Twins. Bacon. Covers the Villiers powered motorcycle & all British powered 'look alikes'. 188 pgs, b&w ill. **£14.95**

Know Thy Beast. Stevens. Comprehensive information on restoration & maintenance of postwar Vincent motor cycles. 259 pgs, 24 ill. **£19.95**

Motorcycle Basics Manual. Haynes. 164 pgs, 394 ill. **£10.63**

Motorcycle Electrical Manual. Haynes. 2nd edition. 125 pgs. **£10.63**

Motorcycle Carburettor Manual, Haynes. app. 100 pgs. **£10.63**

Motorcycle Workshop Practice Manual, Haynes. App. 128 pgs. **£10.63**

Motorcycle Restorer's Workshop Companion. Purnell. The complete guide to techniques & tools for bike restoration & repairs. 160 pgs, 150 b&w ill. **£12.99**

Tuning for Speed. Irving. 6th Ed. How to increase the performance of motorcycle engines for touring, racing & competition. 265 pgs. **£24.95**

VIDEOS:

Castrol History of Motorcycle Racing. Vol 1. How it all began and the TT. 60 mins **£10.99**

Castrol History of Motorcycle Racing. Vol 2. Birth of the GP & the Japanese arrival. 72 mins. **£10.99**

Castrol History of Motorcycle Racing. Vol 3. The other champions & pressure, money & the need to win. 60 mins. ..**£10.99**

Harley Magic. The bike, the legend, the lifestyle. 55 mins. **£10.99**

Tribute to Bob McIntyre. The Northwest 200, 1958. The Right Line 1960. 40 mins.... ....**£17.99**

Motorcycling. Britains Golden Years. Action, fun & nostalgia. 54 mins. **£13.45**

I.O.M. TT. 93. All the best action. 60 mins. **£12.99**

A Place in History. 1993 TT Long Review. Thrilling action. 100 mins. **£16.99**

DIRECTORY OF MUSEUMS

The National Motorcycle Museum:
Coventry Road, Solihull, West Midlands.
Tel: 021-704 2784.

Set in the heart of England's countryside at the centre of the motorway network, the National Motorcycle Museum is a living monument to the once world-dominating British motorcycle industry.

The original concept was conceived nearly 20 years ago: a dream to establish a permanent tribute to Norton. Gradually, the idea came to encompass the whole of the British Motorcycle industry, and the National Motorcycle Museum was born.

Thanks to a loan from one of the founding trustees, a site of some 3.4 hectares was purchased just south of Birmingham, and building began in September 1982. Solicitors formed a charitable trust, and the Museum opened its doors to the public on October 21 1984.

Purpose built to blend into its rural surroundings, the Museum's extensively glass construction floods natural light into the five halls, spectacularly displaying the exhibits. Out of the 650 machines on show, over 95% are owned by the Museum, the remainder are on loan from other collections or private owners across the world.

Potential acquisitions are researched, investigated and 'handled' by the Museum's worldwide network of agents and contacts. Restoration work is then carried out by enthusiasts throughout the country, all of them painstakingly precise in the mechanics, engineering requirements and historical accuracy of each machine they work on. A great many of them work in private workshops for the Museum as a 'labour of love', and they are all, in some way, veterans of the British motorcycle industry.

A fully licensed restaurant, souvenir shop full of motorcycling memorabilia, free car parking and its accessibility to all modes of transport make the National Motorcycle Museum ideally placed to remain a world-beating display of a world-beating industry.

Open every day from 10am-6pm. Take Junction 6 of the M42 and the A45, opposite the National Exhibition Centre. Birmingham International Airport and Railway are minutes away and the No. 900 bus from Birmingham City centre stops right outside.

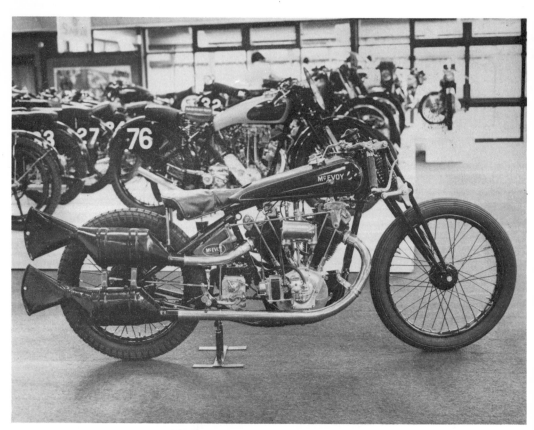

*1927 McEvoy 980cc Motorcycle, V-twin, sporting a striking pair of genuine Brooklands silencers, on display at the **National Motorcycle Museum.***

Battlesbridge Motorcycle Museum:
Battlesbridge Antiques Centre, Maltings Road,
Battlesbridge, Essex. Tel: 0268 769392.
Forty classic machines in a small informal
'museum'. Open Sundays 10am-1pm. Adults £1,
children free.

Birmingham Museum of Science & Industry:
Newhall Street, Birmingham B3 1RZ. Tel: 021-
235 1651.
A small collection of motorcycles right in the heart
of the city.
Open Monday to Saturday 9.30am-5pm. Sunday
2pm- 5pm. Closed December 25-26, and January
1. Admission free.

Bristol Industrial Museum: Princes Wharf, City
Docks, Bristol BS1 4RN. Tel: 0272 251470.
Small collection of Bristol-made Douglas
machines, including the only surviving V4 of 1908.
There is also a 1972 Quasar.
Open Saturday to Wednesday 10am-1pm and
2pm-5pm. Closed Thursdays and Fridays, also
Good Friday, December 25-27 and January 1.
Adults £2, under 16s free.

Brooklands Museum: The Clubhouse,
Brooklands Road, Weybridge, Surrey. Tel: 0932
857381.
The birthplace of British motorsport and aviation,
Brooklands has half-a-dozen motorcycles on
display.
Open Saturday and Sunday 10am-4pm. Guided
tours at 10.30am and 2pm on Tuesdays,
Wednesdays and Thursdays. Adults £4, OAPs and
students £3, children £2.

Grampian Transport Museum: Alford,
Aberdeenshire, Scotland. Tel: 09755 62292.
Collection of 30-40 machines ranging from a 1902
Beeston Humber to a Norton F1. Mods and
Rockers caff display with Triton and Triumph
Tina scooter. Competition section includes 1913
Indian twin and 1976 Rob North replica Trident
racer.
Open March 28-October 31, 10am-5pm. Adults
£2.30, children 80p, OAPs £1.50, family ticket £5.

Haynes Sparkford Motor Museum: Sparkford,
Yeovil, Somerset BA22 7LH. Tel: 0963 40804.
Collection of 28 machines from a 1914 BSA
onwards at the home of Britain's best known
motorcycle book publisher. Video theatre. Large
bookshop.
Open Monday to Sunday 9.30am-5.30pm. Closed
December 25-26 and January 1. Adults £3.50,
OAPs £3, children £2.20.

Midland Motor Museum: Stourbridge Road,
Bridgnorth, Shropshire. Tel: 0746 761761.
Owned by Morris, the oil company, this collection
includes 50 motorcycles.
Open every day in July, August and September
10.30am-5pm, and Saturdays, Sundays and Bank
Holidays 11am-4pm. Adults £3.50, OAPs £2.80,
children 5-16 £1.75, family ticket £9.95.

Murray's Motorcycle Museum: Bungalow
Corner, TT Course, Isle of Man. Tel: 0624 861719.
Collection of 140 machines, including Hailwood's
250cc Mondial racer and the amazing 500cc 4
cylinder roadster designed by John Wooler.
Open May to September 10am-5pm. Adults £2,
OAPs and children £1.

Museum of British Road Transport: St. Agnes
Lane, Hales Street, Coventry. Tel: 0203 832425.
Collection includes 65 motorcycles, with local firms
such as Coventry Eagle, Coventry Victor, Francis
Barnett, Triumph and Rudge well represented.
Close to city centre. Open every day except

December 24-26, 10am-5pm. Adults £2.50,
children, OAPs and unemployed £1.50.

Museum of Transport: Kelvin Hall, 1 Bunhouse
Road, Glasgow G3 8DP. Tel: 041-357 3929.
Small collection of motorcycles includes
Automobile Association BSA combination.
Open Monday to Saturday 10am-5pm. Sunday
11am-5pm. Closed December 25 and January 1.
Admission free.

The Myreton Motor Museum: Aberlady, East
Lothian, Scotland. Tel: 08757 288.
Small collection of motorcycles includes 1926 350cc
Chater-Lea racer and Egli Vincent.
Open Easter to October 10am-5pm and October to
Easter 10am-6pm. Closed December 25 and
January 1. Adults £2, children 50p.

The National Motor Museum: Beaulieu, Hants.
Tel: 0590 612123/612345.
Important motorcycle collection. Reference and
photographic libraries.
Open Easter to September 10am-6pm, October to
Easter 10am-5pm. Closed December 25. Adults
£6.75, OAPs/students £5.25, children £4.75
(includes Museum, rides and drives, Monastic Life
Exhibition and entry to Palace House and
grounds).

Royal Museum of Scotland: Chambers Street,
Edinburgh, Scotland. Tel: 031-225 7534.
Small display of engines and complete machines
includes the world's first 4 cylinder motorcycle, an
1895 Holden.
Open Monday to Saturday 10am-5pm. Sunday
2pm-5pm. Closed December 25, January 1.
Admission free.

Sammy Miller Museum: Gore Road, New Milton,
Hants. Tel: 0425 619696.
The former trials champion and road racer has
assembled a display of engines, artefacts and
complete machines that the visitor can examine at
very close quarters. The display of over 200
machines will shortly be augmented by a 1957
250cc dohc Mondial racer and a W. E. Brough flat
twin.
Open every day 10.15am-4.30pm. Closed
December 25. Adults £2.50, children £2.

The Science Museum: Exhibition Road, South
Kensington, London SW7. Tel: 071-589 3456.
Interesting collection of engines and complete
machines, including cutaway BSA A10 and
Yamaha XS1100. Recent additions to displays
include 1940 500cc BMW and 1969 Honda CB750.
Open Monday to Saturday 10am-6pm. Sunday
11am-6pm. Closed December 24-26. Adults £4,
OAPs and children £2.10, disabled free.
The bulk of the Science Museum's motorcycle
collection is stored at **Wroughton Airfield** near
Swindon, Wilts. Tel: 0793 814466.

Stanford Hall Motorcycle Museum: Stanford
Hall, Lutterworth, Leics. Tel: 0788 860250.
The collection is strong on older machines and
racers.
Open Saturdays, Sundays, Bank Holiday Mondays
and following Tuesdays Easter to September,
2.30pm-6pm. (12am-6pm when a special event is
taking place.) Admission to grounds: Adults £1.60,
children 70p. Motorcycle Museum: Adults 90p,
children 20p.

INDEX TO ADVERTISERS

ARE Ltd...End Paper
Benton, Keith ....End Paper
Big 4 Motorcycle Engineering..................133
Charlies Motorcycles 107
Charnwood Classic Restorations 134
Chester UK Ltd....................................6
Classic Bike Spares 133
Conqueror Industries Ltd............End Paper
Finishing Touch 133
Footman James & Co Ltd..........................2
Francis Motors Ltd, Joe ....End Paper
Freeman Motors, Michael 25
Haggis, L W..29
Holloways ....End Paper
Mitchell & Co, Don 134
Motorcycle Insurance Services..................12
MZ Motorcycles GB Ltd................End Paper
Norton Owners Club..................................73
Oxney Motorcycles...................................2
P J Promotions....................................142
RTS Auctions Ltd 2
Skipsey Scooter Spares, Rob ....End Paper
Sotheby's ....Back cover
Tiernan, Andy 134
Truro Auction Centre....................End Paper
UK Motorcycle Exports-Imports ..End Paper
Verralls (Handcross) Ltd............................81
Vintage Motor Cycle Club Ltd 134
Wilson's 133

Anon, Manx Norton Featherbed, oil, 32 x 24in (81 x 61cm), framed and glazed.
£50-100 *S*

A
Abingdon motorcycles 33
  King Dick 3hp (1912) 33
Acme motorcycles 13
  57cc solo (1913) 13
AEL motorcycles 13
  348cc (1922) 13
Aermacchi motorcycles 13, 114
  250cc Ala d'Oro Racing (1964) 114
  350 Sprint Solo (1972) 13
  350cc Racer (1962) 114
Aermacchi/Harley-Davidson motorcycles 90
  Ala d'Oro 350cc Racing (1969) 90
AJS motorcycles 13-16, 33, 114
  7R 350cc (1950) 15; (1952) 33
  7R 350cc (1953) with 1949 engine 15
  7R 350cc Racing (1949/50, 1961) 114
  14 250cc (1959) 16
  16MS 350cc (1953) 15
  18 500cc (1952) 15
  18S 500cc (1952) 16
  18S 'Green Laner' 500cc (1953) 16
  22 250cc (1936) 14
  30 Spring Twin 600cc (1957) 15
  50cc Solo and Sidecar (child's vehicle) 16
  250cc (1931) 14
  350cc (1927) 13
  350cc Model 16 Replica Trials (1950) 114
  B1 650cc (1960) 16
  B6 350cc (1934) 15
  H6 350cc (1927) 33
  H8 500cc (1927) with Swallow No. 2 Sidecar (1924) 14
Ariel motorcycles 17-19, 33, 91, 115
  350cc Racing 115
  600cc Solo (1946) 17
  Arrow 250cc (1961) 19; (1962) 18
  Huntmaster 650cc (1955) 18
  Leader 250cc (1963, 1964) 19
  Model A 550cc (1930) 17
  Model VH 500cc Red Hunter (1955) 33
  NH Red Hunter 350cc (1948) 18
  Red Hunter 350cc (1939) 17
  Sports Arrow 250cc (1963) 19
  Square Four 4G 995cc (1948) 17
  Square Four 1000cc (1959) 19
  Square Four Mk I 1000cc (1949) 17; (1951) 18
  Square Four Mk II 1000cc Combination with Watsonian Sidecar (1956) 18; (1957) 19
  W/NG 350cc (1942) 91
art 129-30
autocycles 93, 124-5
B
Baker motorcycles 20
  250cc (1928) 20
BAT motorcycles 20
  Model No. 3 8hp 964cc Combination (1912) 20
Beardmore motorcycles 34
  Precision 350cc (1920) 34
Benelli motorcycles 20, 34
  650S Tornado (1979) 20
  750 SEI (1977) 20, 34
bicycles 93, 124
BMW motorcycles 21-2, 34, 121
  R25/2 245cc (1952) 21
  R50 490cc (1959) 21
  R50 Combination (1958) 21
  R51 500cc (1940) 21
  R69 600cc (1959) 34
  R75 746cc Military Combination (1943) 121
  R75/5 750cc (1973) 22
  R80 RT 800cc (1987) 22
Bradbury motorcycles 22, 34
  500cc (1912) 22
  500cc and Sidecar (1912) 34
Brough Superior motorcycles 22, 35
  680 (1928) 22
  SS80 and Launch Sidecar (1938) 22 SS100 (1938) 35
BSA motorcycles 23-31, 35-7, 91, 115, 121
  4hp Combination (1918) 23
  500cc DBD Gold Star (1959) 28
  500cc and Sidecar (1927) 23
  500cc Solo (1925) 23
  551cc (1924) 24
  986cc (1928) 23
  A7SS 500cc (1959) 28
  A10 Cafe Racer 650cc Solo

(1990) 37
  A10 Super Road Rocket (1958) 28
  A65 Firebird 654cc Scrambler (1971) 30
  A65 Thunderbolt 650cc (1970) 37
  A65L Cafe Racer 650cc Solo (1964) 36
  A65L NorBSA Cafe Racer 650cc Solo (1988) 37
  A65T Thunderbolt 650cc (1970) 37
  B2 250cc (1935) 24
  B20 250cc (1937) 24
  B25 Fleetstar 250cc (1971) 30
  B31 350cc Solo (1954) 26
  B33 500cc (1948) 25
  B34 Trials 500cc (1949) 115
  B40 350cc (1963) 36
  B40 WD 350cc (1967) 91; (1968) 121
  B44 Victor 441cc (1968) 29
  Bantam 125cc (1954) 25
  Bantam 175cc (1969) 29
  Bantam D1 125cc (1949) 35; (1952) 25; (1958) 27; (1961) 28; (1962) 29
  Bantam D14/4 Sports 175cc (1968) 36
  C11 250cc (1953) 35
  C12 250cc (1956, 1957) 27; (1960) 28
  C15 250cc (1962) 29
  DB Gold Star 350cc (1960) 28
  Firebird 650cc (1972) 31
  Gold Star 500cc (1954) 26
  Golden Flash (1955) 36
  M20 500cc (1943) 91
  M20 EX-WD 500cc (1940) 25
  M20 WD 500cc (1940) 25
  M21 600cc (1957) 27
  Rocket 3 750cc (1972) 31
  S30 - 19 'Light' 4 93hp 500cc (1930) 24
  Star Twin A7 500cc (1952) 26
  US Model A65L Spitfire Mk IV Solo (1968) 29
  Victor/Rickman 441cc Solo (1988) 31
  ZB31 350cc (1954) 25
C
Calthorpe motorcycles 32
  150cc Solo (1921) 32
  348cc (1928) 32
Can-Am motorcycles 121
  250cc Bombardier ex-British Army Solo (1980) 121
clothing 94, 130
competition motorcycles 114-20
Cossack motorcycles 121
  Model M66 and Sidecar (1975) 121
Cotton motorcycles 32, 37
  750cc (1935) 32
  Telstar Mk II 247cc Racing (1964) 37
Coventry motorcycles 32
  Eagle K2 250cc (1934) 32
D
Dandy motorcycles 32
  Miniature Motorcycle (1980) 32
DMW motorcycles 32
  Deemster 250cc (1965) 32
Douglas motorcycles 38, 49-50
  2.75hp (1921) 49
  4hp Solo (1920) 49
  4hp Twin Cylinder (1920) 38
  500cc (1935) 50
  D29 350cc (1929) 49
  EW 26 350cc Solo (1926) 49
  EW B29 350cc (1929) 49
  Mark IV 350cc (1952) 49
Ducati motorcycles 38, 50-1, 115, 160
  Junior 160cc 51
  250cc Racing 115
  500GTL 497cc 2 Cylinder (1975, 1978) 50
  900cc (1977) 50
  Desmo 750cc (1974) 38
  Saxon-Brancato 350R (1988) 38
  V-twin 851cc (1989) 51
E
EMC Puch motorcycles 51
  125cc 51
ephemera 94-6, 130-2
  magazines 94, 130-1
  miscellaneous 132
  posters 95-6, 131
  programmes 131
Excelsior motorcycles 38, 52
  148cc (1934) 52
  250cc (1925) 38
  Manxman 250cc (1936) 52
  Manxman Special (1936) 52

Solo Racing (1936) 52
  Talismara Twin 250cc 2-Stroke 52, 115
F
FB/Mondial motorcycles 39, 115
  125cc Bialbero Racing (1955) 39, 115
Francis Barnett motorcycles 39, 53, 115
  1.5hp (1924) 39
  Cruiser 250cc (1939) 53
  Falcon 74 197cc (1955) 53
  Falcon 81 197cc (1959) 53
  Falcon 87 199cc (1960) 53
  TS Model M/C 82
  25C Trials (1960) 115
G
Gilera motorcycles 53-4
  Giubileo 98cc 4 Stroke 54
  Saturno 500cc (1952) 53
Greeves motorcycles 115
  Model 24SAS Hawkstone Scrambler (1959) 115
H
Harley-Davidson motorcycles 39, 54-5, 91, 121-2
  11hp and Sidecar (1915) 54
  'D' FXR Pursuit Glide 1340cc (1989) 55
  FLH Hydra Glide 1207cc (1954) 54
  FLHTC 1340cc Classic Electra Glide (1984) 55
  FLTC 1340cc Classic Electra Glide (1981) 55
  'P' Servicar 750cc (1964) 54
  Sportster 1200cc (1989) 39
  Wide Glide Softail 1340cc (1988) 55
  WLA 45 750cc Military (1949) 121
  WLA Military Police (1942) 122
  WLC 750cc (1943) 91
Harris motorcycles 55
  Magnum One 1198cc 55
  Magnum Two 120hp 1085cc (1983) 55
Healey motorcycles 56
  1000/4 997cc (1976) 56
helmets 94
Hesketh motorcycles 56
  V1000 (1984) 56
Honda motorcycles 39, 56-60, 126
  49cc 'Monkey Bike' (1968) 57
  C72 250cc (1962) 56
  C92 125cc (1962) 56
  C114 50cc (1964) 126
  CB77 305cc (1964) 57
  CB77 Super Sport (1963) 56
  CB92 Benly Super Sport 125cc 60; (1964) 57
  CB250 60
  CB250 G5 (1976) 58
  CB750 (1969/70) 57
  CB750 K2 (1972) 57
  CB750 KO (1969) 57
  CB750 736cc (1970) 39
  CB750F Super Sport (1976) 58
  CB1100 RB (1981) 59
  CBXC1000 (1987) 58
  Dunstall 900cc (1973) 57
  Goldwing 1200cc (1988) 59
  Goldwing GL1000 (1977) 58
  Goldwing GL1100 (1982) 59
  Goldwing GL1100 DXC 83hp 1085cc (1982) 59
  Modern Tourer Goldwing Aspencade 1200cc (1988) 59
  RS 125W 1980C 59
  XL250 (1974) 58
HRD motorcycles 60
  Comet 500cc (1935) 60
Humber motorcycles 40, 60
  2.75hp 349cc (1924) 60
  350cc (1927) 40, 60
  500cc (1912) 60
Husqvarna motorcycles 61
  500cc Motocross (1970) 61
I
Indian motorcycles 40, 61, 122
  7hp Single Speed 1000cc (1913) 61
  1000cc (1913) 40
  Chief 74 cu in 1200cc (1946) 61
  Model 741A Military (1942) 122
Itom motorcycles 116
  49cc Racing (1952) 116
Ivy motorcycles 40, 61
  2.75hp (1926) 61
  224cc (1921) 40, 61
J
James motorcycles 40, 61, 122
  197cc 'Captain' (1955) 61
  Comet 98cc (1950) 40

ML 125cc (1943) 122
Jawa motorcycles 62, 116
  350 with Velorex Sidecar (1986) 62
  DT 500cc Union Jack Anniversary Speedway (1980) 116
  Model 638 350cc (1992) 62
K
Kawasaki motorcycles 62
  H1A 500cc (1971) 62
  Police Z1000 (1981) 62
  Z1B 903cc (1975) 62
KTM motorcycles 63
  250cc Motorcross (1980) 63
L
Laverda motorcycles 63, 116
  750 (1968) 63
  750 SFC Racing (1971) 116
Levis motorcycles 63
  Model K 2.5hp (1924) 63
LMC motorcycles 63
  550cc (1914) 63
M
magazines 94, 130-1
Maico motorcycles 41, 64, 116
  Blizzard (1957) 64
  Mobil 200cc fully enclosed (1958) 64
  Model 501 Motorcross (1970) 64
  RS 125 R 125cc Racing (1975) 116
  Taifun 400cc (1957) 41
Maserati motorcycles 116
  SS50 (1952) 116
Matchless motorcycles 41, 64-6, 92, 117, 122
  650cc (1962) 117
  G2 250cc (1936) 64
  G3 350cc (1941) 92
  G3L 350cc (1948) 41
  G3L 350cc Military (1941) 122
  G3LC 350cc Solo (1953) 41
  G3LS 350cc (1955) 65; (1957) 41
  G9 500cc (1954) 65
  G12 650cc (1960) 65
  G12 CSR 650cc (1961) 65
  G80 (1987) 66
  G80 CS 500cc Scramble (1963) 117
  G80S 500cc (1952) 64
  Model H 8hp and Sidecar (1921) 64
  L/3 350cc (1924) 122
  Model M 591cc (1926) 122
  Rotax 500cc (1989) 66
memorabilia 129-32
  art 95-6, 129-30
  clothing 94, 130
  ephemera 130-2
military motorcycles 121-3
Minerva motorcycles 66
  2.25hp (1903) 66
models 94
mopeds 44-5, 93, 126-8
Morgan motorcycles 66
  1100cc JAP engine, overhead valve (1932) 66
Moto Guzzi motorcycles 42, 67-8, 123
  192cc (1955) 67
  Airone Sport 250cc (1952, 1953) 67
  Astore 500cc (1952, 1953) 67
  Falcone GT 500cc (1964) 67
  Falcone Sport 500cc (1953) 42
  Super Alce 500cc Military (1945/46) 123
  T3 850cc (1976) 42
  V7 750cc Combination (1970) 68
  V50 II 493cc (1980) 68
Moto Morini motorcycles 68
  Strada 3.5 350cc 68
Moto Parilla motorcycles 117
  250 Grand Prix Racing (1947) 117
Motobecane motorcycles 66
  Lightweight (1964) 66
motorcycle parts 132
motorised bicycles 124-5
MV Agusta motorcycles 68-70, 123
  125 Sport (1976) 70
  125cc Lungo (1952) 68
  149cc (1960) 68
  250B 250cc (1969) 69
  250cc Raid (1957) 68
  350GT (1977) 70
  350GT 350cc Police (1975) 123
  Sport Drum Brake Type 214 (1969) 69
  Turismo 150cc (1963) 69
N
New Imperial motorcycles 70
  350cc (1926) 70
Norman motorcycles 70

250cc Sports (1960) 70
Norton motorcycles 37, 42-3, 71-5, 117-18
30M 490cc (1956) 118
350cc (1936) 42
750 'S' (1969) 74
Atlas 750cc (1962, 1965) 73
BVR Cafe Racer 1000cc Solo (1988) 43
Classic 600cc (1988) 74
Classic Rotary 588cc (1985) 75
Commando 850cc (1976) 74
Commando Fastback 750cc (1968) 73;
(1971) 43
Commando Mk III (1977) 75
CS1 500cc (1928) 117
Dominator 88SS 500cc (1963) 43
Dominator 99 600cc (1956) 71
Dominator 99SS Cafe Racer (1961) 72
Dominator 650 SS (1967) 74
Dominator Model 77 600cc (1958) 71
Electra 400cc (1964) 73
Harmless Vintage Sprinter 798cc Solo (1991) 75
International (1958) 72
Jubilee 250cc (1959) 43; (1961) 72
Manx 40M 350cc (1958) 118
Manx 350cc (1957) 42
Manx 500cc Racing (1961) 118
Manx Garden Gate (1944) 117
Manx Special 500cc 118
Manx/International 499cc (1956) 117
Model 18 500cc (1946, 1951) 71
Model 30 International 490cc (1949) 117
Model 50 350cc (1959, 1960) 72
Navigator 350cc (1962) 73
NorBSA Cafe Racer A65L 650cc Solo (1988) 37
NSU motorcycles, HK101 Kettenkraftrad Tracked (1942) 123

O
O.E.C. motorcycles 76
1000cc (1922) 76
Overseas motorcycles 44, 76
490cc (1914) 76
490cc Combination (1914) 44

P
Panther motorcycles 44, 76
100 600cc (1948) 76
120 650cc (1961) 76
250cc (1936) 76
M100 600cc (1952) 76
Model 85 498cc (1930) 44
Parilla Olympia motorcycles 77
115cc 160 77
posters 95-6, 131
programmes 131
Puch motorcycles 77
250cc (1965) 77

Q
Quadrant motorcycles 77
Combination (1919) 77

R
Raleigh motorcycles 44, 77-9
2.75hp (1923) 45; (1924) 78
250cc Sports (1928) 79
350cc Sport (1925) 78
Model 6 348cc (1924) 77
Model 15 De Luxe 248cc (1929) 78
Reliant motorcycles 45, 79
Regal Mk II 747cc (1956) 45
Regal Mk III 747cc Coupe (1956) 79
Rex Acme motorcycles 45, 79
Rexette 5hp Forecar (1904) 79
Rexette 7hp Forecar (1905) 45
TT8 Sports Replica 350cc (1928) 79
Rickman motorcycles 79, 118
750cc Racing (1973) 118
Metisse Triumph T120R 650cc (1969) 79
Triumph Metisse 650cc (1973) 79
Royal Enfield motorcycles 46, 80, 90, 92, 97, 118, 123
1 Bullet Scrambler (1953) 90, 118
2.25hp (1921) 80; (1922) 97
150cc Prince (1960) 97
248cc Trials (1961) 118
499cc (1948) 97
'Flying Flea' Model RE (1940) 92, 123
Meteor Minor Sports 500cc

(1960) 97
Model 180 6hp 770cc (1914) 80
Model 200 2.25hp 225cc (1921) 80
Model K 976cc (1931) 80
Model KX 1140cc and Sidecar (1939) 46
Model LF 500cc Trials (1933) 118
Single Cylinder 500cc Twin Port Model LF (1933) 97
WD/C 350cc (1940) 92
WD/CO 350cc (1943) 123
WD/RE 125cc (1944) 92
Rudge motorcycles 46, 98-9, 119
350cc (1930) 98
500cc (1911) 46
500cc Racing (1929) 119
Four 500cc (1925) 98
Rapid 250cc (1937) 46, 98; (1938) 99
Special 500cc (1928) 98; (1938) 99
Special Combination (1936) 98
Ulster GP 500cc Racing (1933) 98

S
Scott motorcycles 46, 99
2 Speed 2 Stroke (1930) 99
Flyer 596cc 'Clubman Special' Solo (1934) 46
TT Replica 500cc (1929) 99
TT Replica 596cc (1930) 99
Seeley motorcycles 100
Weslake 750 (1975) 100
signs 96, 132
Singer motorcycles 100
500cc (1912) 100
Sun motorcycles 100
98cc (1953) 100
Sunbeam motorcycles 47, 100-2, 119
90TT Model 500cc (1929) 47
95R 500cc Racing (1935) 119
500cc Combination (1922) 100
Lion 598cc (1939) 101
Little 95R 250cc Racing (1933) 119
Model 1 2.75hp (1927) 47
Model 1 Roadster 347cc (1923/24) 100
Model 8 350cc (1928) 101
Model 9 500cc (1925) 100; (1934) 101
Model 9 500cc Racing, ex-Achille Varzi (1924) 119
Model 9 TT Replica 500cc Racing (1926) 119
Model 80 Works TT 350cc Racing (1928) 119
Model 90 493cc (1927/28) 101
Model 90 TT Replica 500cc Racing (1927) 119
S7 (1954) 47
S7 500cc (1947) 102; (1950) 101-2
S8 500cc (1950, 1956) 102
Sprint 500cc (1924) 119
Sprint Special 3.5hp 500cc (1926) 119
Works Model 90 TT 500cc Racing (1927, 1928) 119
Suzuki motorcycles 47-8, 90, 102, 120
FZ50 50cc (1982) 128
GSX 1000 SZ Katana 997cc (1982) 48
GT 500 (1976) 102
RG500 Mk 3 2 Stroke 120
RG500 Mk 5 Racing (1979) 120
RG500 Solo Racing 120
RG500 XR45 500cc Racing (1983) 97
RG 500cc (1985) 47

T
tricycles 126
Triton motorcycles 48, 102
650cc (1950/60, 1991) 102
650cc Special (1960) 102
750cc (1960) 48
Triumph motorcycles 48, 82-7, 103-8, 120
3.5hp 470cc (1909) 48, 103
3TA 490cc (1958) 105
3TA Type 21 350cc (1960, 1964) 106
3TU 350cc (1960) 82
5T Speed Twin (1938) 104
5TA Trials 500cc (1962) 90
6T Thunderbird 650cc (1951) 106; (1959) 105
120 Thunderbird 650cc (1965) 106
225cc (1918) 103
350cc Prototype (1965) 83

499cc (1910, 1913) 103
500cc (1914) 48
500cc Sports (1925) 104
650cc (1961) 106
750cc T150 Trident (1970, 1972) 107
750cc Trident (1975) 107
Bonneville 650cc (1964) 83
Bonneville 750cc (1981) 108
Bonneville T120 650cc (1968, 1970) 107; (1972) 85
Bonneville T120 Solo (1968) 84
Bonneville T140 750cc (1980) 86, 108; (1981) 87
Bonneville T140V 750cc 108; (1979) 86
Bonneville Thruxton T120 650cc (1966) 120
Cardinal 3 cylinder (1970s) 86
Hurricane 750cc (1973) 85
L2/1 249cc (1935) 120
Model H 550cc (1917) 103
Silver Jubilee Bonneville 750cc (1977) 108
Speed Twin 500cc (1938) 82; (1948) 105; (1951) 82
T20 Tiger Cub (1958) 105
T20C Tiger Cub Trials 200cc (1959) 105
T90 Tiger 350cc Solo (1964) 83
T100 Tiger Daytona 500cc (1970) 107
T150V Trident 750cc Solo (1974) 85
T160V Trident Solo (1976) 86
Terrier T15 150cc (1954) 105
Thunderbird 650cc (1959) 83
Thunderbird Sprung Hub 650cc Solo (1950) 104
Tiger 90 350cc (1963) 106
Tiger 100 500cc (1946, 1947) 104
Tiger 500cc (1936) 104
Tiger Cub 200cc (1963) 106
TR5T 500cc (1973) 85
TR6R 650cc (1972) 107
TR7RV 750cc (1979) 108
TR7V 750cc (1972) 84
TR65 650cc Thunderbird (1981) 108; (1982) 87
Trail Blazer SS 250cc (1971) 84
Trophy (1970) 84
TRW 500cc Display Team (1953) 105

V
Velocette motorcycles 87-9, 109-11
275cc (1920) 109
GTP 250cc (1932) 109; (1937, 1939) 110
KTS 350cc (1933) 109; (1934) 87, 110
KTT Mk I (1930) 109
LE 192cc (1955, 1968) 111
LE 200cc (1953) 110; (1955) 88; (1958) 89
Mac 350cc (1938) 88
Mk VIII 350cc (1950) 88
Model K 350cc (1926) 109
Model KNSS (1930) 87
MOV 250cc (1934) 110
Thruxton 500cc (1968) 111
Valiant 192cc (1952) 88
Veloce 293cc (1913) 109
Venom 500cc (1959) 110
Venom Clubman's 500cc (1959) 111
Viper Clubman's 350cc (1959) 111
Vogue 192cc (1964) 89
Vincent motorcycles 89, 111-12, 120
Black Shadow 1000cc (1952) 89; (1953) 112
Comet 500cc (1951) 112
Grey Flash, The Eppynt Racer (1949) 120
Rapide 1000cc (1951) 112
Rapide 1000cc Series C (1949, 1950) 111; (1952) 112
Series D Open Rapide (1956) 89
Vindec motorcycles 113
300cc (1926) 113

W
WSK motorcycles 113
175cc (1972) 113

Y
Yamaha motorcycles 113, 120
250cc Racing (1970) 120
YDS 2 250cc (1964) 113
YZ 495cc (1981) 113
YZ Model 250cc Racing (1970) 120

Z
Zenith motorcycles 113
V Twin 680cc (1927) 113
Zundapp motorcycles 113, 123
200S (1958) 113
KS 750cc (1943) 123

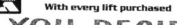